Welcome to
BASIC
Grammar

2

KUMSUNG

About This Book

개념 학습

✚ 초등학생이 꼭 알아야 할 문법 개념을 쉽게 설명해요.

모바일 강의 예시

친구들의 문법 도우미! 니콜 선생님의 쉽고 재미있는 설명을 들으면 문법 개념이 머리에 쏙쏙! 문법 실력은 쑥쑥!

PC www.englishbuddy.kr에서도 볼 수 있어요.

문제 풀이

✚ Quick Check-Up ➡ 다양한 유형의 exercise ➡ Fun Wrap-Up 순으로 문제를 제시하여 체계적으로 학습할 수 있어요.

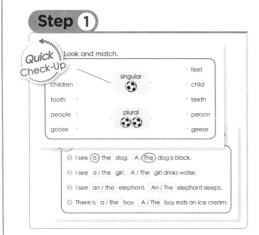

간단한 문제를 풀어보며 문법 개념을 잘 이해했는지 확인해요.

다양한 유형의 문제를 풀어보며 실력을 다져요.

미로 찾기, 색칠하기 등 재미있는 활동으로 학습한 내용을 복습하며 마무리해요.

Contents 2

Chapter

부사와
형용사(2)

5

I can do it!

22 부사 1

부사의 역할

❁ 부사는 형용사나 동사, 또 다른 부사를 더 자세히 설명해 주고,
주로 '~게, ~하게'라고 해석해요.

I eat **fast**.　　　　　　He studies **hard**.

This is **very** hot.　　　　You are **too** young.

❁ 부사에는 다음과 같은 것들이 있어요.

언제	soon	late	early	now
어디서	inside	outside	here	there
어떻게	easily	hard	slowly	quickly
얼마나	only	too	very	really

Quick Check-Up ― **Circle the correct** *adverbs*.

• adverb 부사

❶
slowly
quickly

❸
inside
outside

❷
kindly
badly

❹
happily
heavily

부사의 역할

A Circle the *adverbs*.

1. I ate pizza (slowly).

2. I make a card easily.

3. He speaks quietly.

4. I have only two pencils.

5. See you later.

6. You speak English well.

7. She comes late.

8. The bird sings beautifully.

B Choose and write.

1. Jack runs _____fast_____. | fast / slow

2. She is _____ pretty. | here / very

3. The kids talk _____. | loudly / up

4. Ann works _____. | really / hard

5. He gets up _____. | early / down

6. I go to bed _____. | late / up

 Help the boy find his puppy.

study hard

very beautiful

study hard

walk fastly

very pretty

study hard

eat fast

run fast

walk slowly

sing happily

pretty very

speak kindly

swim good

work hard

dance well

부사의 위치

❋ 부사는 일반동사 뒤에 오거나 형용사나 부사 앞에 와요.

• 일반동사 뒤에 오는 경우

He **walks slowly**.
일반동사

• 형용사 앞에 오는 경우

That is a **very tall** building.
형용사

• 부사 앞에 오는 경우

They work **so hard**.
부사

a tall building   a very tall building

 Quick Check-Up Circle the correct ones.

① She {(jumps high.) / high jumps.}

② You are {so kind. / kind so.}

③ They {late come. / come late.}

④ He {well speaks Korean. / speaks Korean well.}

⑤ I like {pizza very much. / very pizza much.}

⑥ She is {very tall. / tall very.}

부사의 위치

A Choose and write.

1 Mom walks _____slowly_____ . | slow / (slowly) |

2 These are _____ interesting. | very / hard |

3 The students speak _____ . | loudly / very |

4 We read it _____ . | quickly / very |

5 Birds sing _____ . | happily / so |

B Unscramble and write.

1 run / The boys / fast.   _The boys run fast._

2 He / very / hard. / studies   _____

3 milk / I / very much. / like   _____

4 Tom / hard. / studies English   _____

5 hop / Frogs / high.   _____

 Make your own story.

I run fast.

I play soccer very well.

I run _____ fast _____.

I do my homework _____.
quickly / carefully

I play soccer _____.
well / badly

I play computer games _____.
well / hard

I ride my bike _____.
carefully / fast

부사의 형태: 규칙형

❀ 부사는 대부분의 형용사에 -ly를 붙여서 만들어요.

대부분의 형용사	-ly	bad → bad**ly** soft → soft**ly** quiet → quiet**ly**
-le로 끝나는 형용사	-le → -ly	gentle → gent**ly** simple → simp**ly**
[자음 +y]로 끝나는 형용사	-y → -ily	happy → happ**ily** heavy → heav**ily**

❀ **good**과 **well**처럼 형용사와 부사의 형태가 전혀 다른 경우도 있어요.

Quick
Check-Up ## Circle the correct ones.

❶ (gently)/ gentlely

❷ busyly / busily

❸ slowly / slowy

❹ queity / quietly

❺ happyly / happily

❻ kindily / kindly

❼ simply / simplely

❽ merrily / merryly

A Look and match.

① good   quietly

② correct   carefully

③ quiet   well

④ careful   simply

⑤ simple   correctly

B Find and write the *adverbs*.

Turtles walk slowly.
Frogs jump high.
Cheetahs run fast.
Birds sing happily.
I see the animals carefully.

high   _____   _____

_____   _____

 Follow and circle.

loudly	angrily	quietly	sadly	loudly
happily	happily	angrily	kindly	easily
(slowly)	slowly	loudly	simply	slowly
angrily	carefully	sadly	quietly	quietly

부사의 형태: 불규칙형

❀ 형용사와 형태가 같은 부사

fast 빠른 → fast 빨리	late 늦은 → late 늦게
high 높은 → high 높게	last 마지막의 → last 마지막으로
early 이른 → early 일찍	hard 열심인 → hard 열심히

❀ -ly를 붙이면 다른 뜻이 되는 부사

hard 열심히 ≠ hardly 거의 ~않는	late 늦게 ≠ lately 최근에
close 가까이 ≠ closely 주의 깊게	high 높이 ≠ highly 높이 평가하여, 매우

Quick Check-Up Circle the correct ones.

① I get up (late) / lately in the morning.

② He works hard / hardly .

③ The dog runs fast / fastly .

④ Come close / closely .

⑤ I jump high / highly .

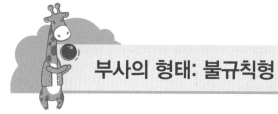

A Change the sentences.

1 I am a fast runner. ➲ I run ____fast____ .

2 He is a careful driver. ➲ He drives _____ .

3 She is a slow swimmer. ➲ She swims _____ .

4 He is a kind teacher. ➲ He teaches _____ .

5 You are a hard worker. ➲ You work _____ .

B Correct and rewrite.

1 She drives her car ~~careful~~. ____carefully____

2 The car moves **slow**. _____

3 John plays football very **good**. _____

4 The team plays tennis **bad**. _____

5 They run **fastly**. _____

Find and circle the words.

```
Q   Q   I   N   L   B   C
Q   U   K   F   A   S   T
Y   D   I   D   T   L   E
F   H   N   C   E   O   A
X   A   D   I   K   W   R
M   R   L   W   E   L   L
H   D   Y   C   M   Y   Y
```

QUICKLY	KINDLY	WELL	HARD
FAST	SLOWLY	EARLY	LATE

빈도부사

빈도부사의 종류

🌸 빈도부사는 어떤 행동을 얼마나 자주 하는지를 나타내는 부사예요.

always 항상　**usually** 보통, 대개　**often** 종종　**sometimes** 때때로　**seldom** 드물게　**rarely** 좀처럼 ~않는　**never** 결코 ~않는

I **usually** stay at home.

I **often** go to the park.

I **sometimes** play soccer.

I **never** do that.

> 단어 자체에 부정의 의미가 있는 seldom, rarely, never는 not과 함께 쓰이지 않아요.

Quick Check-Up　## Check the *frequency adverbs*.　• frequency adverb 빈도부사

☐ often　　☐ sometimes

☑ always　　☐ simply

☐ never　　☐ usually

☐ quietly　　☐ kindly

☐ seldom　　☐ rarely

빈도부사의 종류

A Circle the *frequency adverbs*.

① I (often) walk to school.

② He never drinks coffee.

③ They sometimes play baseball.

④ We usually meet in the library.

⑤ I rarely eat seafood.

B Complete your own story.

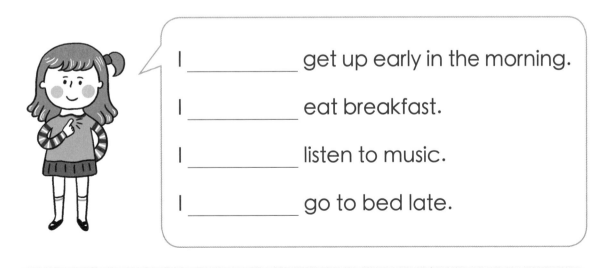

I _____ get up early in the morning.

I _____ eat breakfast.

I _____ listen to music.

I _____ go to bed late.

| always | usually | often |
| sometimes | rarely | never |

 Cut and paste.

★ ★ ★ ★ ★ ★ 　 always

★ ★ ★ ★ ★ ☆

★ ★ ★ ★ ☆ ☆

★ ★ ★ ☆ ☆ ☆

★ ★ ☆ ☆ ☆ ☆

★ ☆ ☆ ☆ ☆ ☆

☆ ☆ ☆ ☆ ☆ ☆

※ 아래와 동일한 카드가 159쪽에 있습니다. 해당 페이지의 카드를 사용하세요.

rarely	sometimes	never	always
often	usually	seldom	

Go to p. 159

빈도부사

빈도부사의 위치

✿ 빈도부사는 be동사의 뒤, 일반동사의 앞에 위치해요.

- be동사 뒤에 오는 경우

  Stella is **always** kind.

  The room is **often** empty.

- 일반동사 앞에 오는 경우

  I **sometimes** clean my room.

  We **often** play computer games.

be동사 + 빈도부사

빈도부사 + 일반동사

Quick Check-Up Circle the correct ones.

① I read often / (often read) books.

② He rarely goes / goes rarely to the movies.

③ She goes always / always goes to bed late.

④ You drink never / never drink milk.

⑤ He is usually / usually is late for school.

A Complete the sentences.

1 I _usually get up_ late on Sunday. (get up, usually)

2 John _____ late for school. (never, is)

3 He _____ on weekends. (travels, often)

4 Susan _____ . (sometimes, cries)

5 We _____ John. (seldom, see)

B Unscramble the sentences.

1 never / Judy / eats / fast food.

Judy never eats fast food.

2 play soccer / We / sometimes / together.

_____

3 milk. / His sister / drinks / always

_____

 Fill in the chart and say.

I usually get up at 8 a.m.

I never get up at 8 a.m.

	Always	Usually	Often	Sometimes	Never
I get up at 8 a.m.					
I clean my room.					
I do my homework.					
I play football with my friends.					
I have dinner at 9 p.m.					
I go to bed at 10 p.m.					

형용사 비교급

형용사-er

⚙ 두 개의 명사를 비교할 때는 형용사의 비교급을 사용해요.

- 형용사-er

The boy is tall**er**.
The girl is short**er**.
The puppy is young**er**.

- more+3음절 이상의 형용사

The question is **more** difficult.
The singer is **more** famous.
These flowers are **more** beautiful.

tall taller

beautiful   **more** beautiful

Quick Check-Up — Check the correct *comparatives*.

• comparative 비교급

- ☐ short – shorter
- ☐ smart – smarter
- ☐ small – more small
- ☐ tall – more tall
- ☐ beautiful – more beautiful
- ☑ old – older
- ☐ young – younger
- ☐ deep – deeper
- ☐ famous – famouser
- ☐ difficult – difficulter

형용사-er

A Look and write.

old	long	older	younger
faster	fast	longer	young

Adjectives

old
_____
_____
_____
_____

Comparatives

older
_____
_____
_____
_____

B Look and write.

1

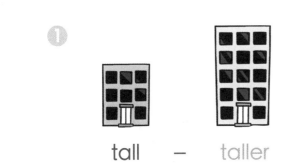

tall – taller
_____

3

slow –
_____

2

long –
_____

4

old –
_____

 Look and write.

①

The monkey is big.

The elephant is bigger.

②

The cat is tall.

_____

③

The mouse is fast.

_____

dog / taller   elephant / bigger   car / faster

형용사 비교급

형용사-er+than, more+형용사+than

❖ 비교급은 두 개 이상의 대상을 비교할 때 사용하고,
[비교급+than+비교 대상] 형태로 나타내요.

Airplanes are fast**er than** buses.

This singer is **more famous than** that singer.

❖ 비교급 만드는 규칙

대부분 형용사	-er	kind → kind**er**
-e로 끝나는 형용사	-r	wise → wise**r**
[단모음+단자음]으로 끝나는 형용사	자음 한 번 더 쓰고 -er	hot → hot**ter**
[자음+y]로 끝나는 형용사	-y → -ier	happy → happ**ier**
3음절 이상의 형용사	more+형용사	important → **more** important

Quick Check-Up

Circle the correct *comparatives.*

• comparative 비교급

① biger / (bigger)

② easyer / easier

③ older / oldder

④ importanter / more important

⑤ fater / fatter

⑥ happyer / happier

⑦ hoter / hotter

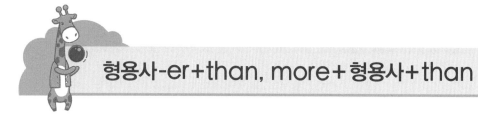

형용사-er+than, more+형용사+than

A Unscramble the sentences.

① bigger / The horse / the dog. / is / than

The horse is bigger than the dog.

② than / My sister / younger / Jane. / is

_____

③ Summer / hotter / is / spring. / than

_____

④ more important / This / than / is / that.

_____

B Correct and rewrite.

① Math is **difficulter** than science.   more difficult

② Suzy is **more smart** than Tom.   _____

③ My room is **cleanner** than yours.   _____

④ Dancing is **funnyer** than singing.   _____

Read and write.

John	Judy	Suzy	Tom
50 years old	45 years old	7 years old	10 years old
170 cm	160 cm	100 cm	130 cm
80 kg	60 kg	17 kg	30 kg

1. John is _____older_____ than Judy. (old)

2. Suzy is _____ than Tom. (young)

3. John is _____ than Suzy. (tall)

4. Suzy is _____ than Tom. (happy)

형용사 최상급

형용사-est

✿ 세 개 이상의 대상을 비교할 때는 최상급을 사용할 수 있어요. 최상급 뒤에 [of+비교 대상] 또는 [in+비교 범위]를 써서 비교의 대상을 제한할 수도 있어요.

· 최상급: [the+최상급+비교 범위] …에서 가장 ~한

This is **the tallest building in the city**.

Tom is **the happiest man of us**.

✿ 형용사의 최상급 만드는 규칙

대부분의 형용사	-est	kind → kind**est**
e로 끝나는 형용사	-st	wise → wise**st**
[단모음+단자음]으로 끝나는 형용사	자음 한 번 더 쓰고 -est	hot → hot**test**
[자음+y]로 끝나는 형용사	-y → -iest	happy → happ**iest**

Quick Check-Up — **Circle the correct *superatives*.**

· superative 최상급

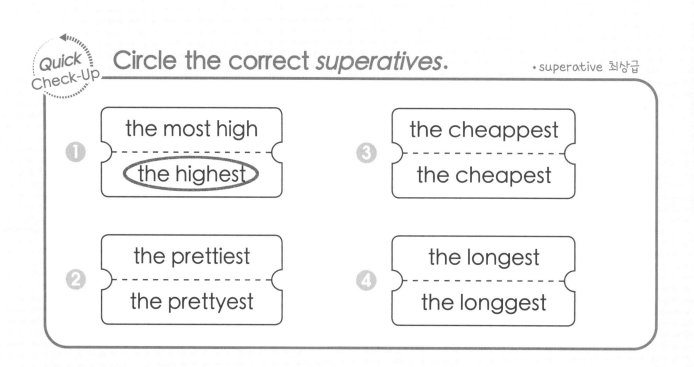

① the most high / ~~the highest~~

② the prettiest / the prettyest

③ the cheappest / the cheapest

④ the longest / the longgest

A Unscramble the sentences.

1. girl / Mary / is / the bravest / in my class.

   Mary is the bravest girl in my class.

2. in my school. / the tallest / Paul / is

   _____

3. The bag / the cheapest / is / in the shop.

   _____

B Look and write.

1.

   The elephant is _the biggest_ .

   big   bigger   biggest

2.

   Mt. Everest is _____.

   high   higher   highest

Answer the questions.

In My Class

① Who is the tallest student in your class?

_____ is _the_ _tallest_ student in my class.

② Who is the shortest student in your class?

_____ is _____ _____ student in my class.

③ Who is the strongest student in your class?

_____ is _____ _____ student in my class.

④ Who has the longest hair in your class?

_____ has _____ _____ _____ in my class.

⑤ Who has the biggest eyes in your class?

_____ has _____ _____ _____ in my class.

형용사 최상급

the most + 형용사

✿ 3음절 이상의 형용사: the most + 형용사

The car is **the most expensive** in the world.

This is **the most interesting** book.

the most expensive car

the most interesting book

✿ -ful, -ous, -ing 등으로 끝나는 형용사

the most care**ful**, the most use**ful**, the most fam**ous**,

the most excit**ing** ...

Quick Check-Up — Check the correct ones.

☑ the most famous   ☐ the most clean

☐ the usefulest   ☐ the beautifulest

☐ the most careful   ☐ the most exciting

☐ the most interesting

the most+형용사

A Unscramble the sentences.

1. is / Science / most / the / difficult / subject.

   Science is the most difficult subject.

2. beautiful / My house / the / most / is / in the town.

   _____

3. in the store. / This bag / expensive / the / is / most

   _____

B Complete the sentences with *superlatives*.

1. February is ___the shortest___ month of the year. (short)

2. Horse riding is _____ sport. (dangerous)

3. Tommy is _____ in the school. (popular)

4. *Star Wars* is _____ in the world. (exciting)

5. This building is _____ in the town. (high)

 Read and write.

Quiz!

Mary is more intelligent than Suzy.

Mary is more intelligent than Judy.

Who is the most intelligent? _____Mary_____

Quiz!

Harry Potter is more interesting than *Star Wars*.

Star Wars is more interesting than *Minions*.

What is the most interesting? _____

Quiz!

Science is more difficult than English.

Math is more difficult than science.

What is the most difficult? _____

A **Choose the correct answers.**

1 I eat _____ .
   ① fast   ② hungry   ③ happy

2 The boys _____ .
   ① running fast   ② fast run   ③ run fast

3 He is a careful driver. → He drives _____ .
   ① care   ② carefully   ③ be careful

4 Math is _____ than science.
   ① difficulter   ② more difficult   ③ difficult

5 The horse is _____ than the dog.
   ① bigger   ② big   ③ more big

B **Fill in the blanks.**

most	than	slowly	very

1 Turtles walk _____ .

2 This is _____ hot.

3 Horse riding is the _____ dangerous sport.

4 John is older _____ Judy.

C Unscramble the sentences.

1   You / too / are / young.

_____

2   play / I / soccer. / sometimes

_____

3   Airplanes / faster / are / buses. / than

_____

4   is / The car / the most / in the world. / expensive

_____

D Answer the questions.

1   Do you eat fast or slowly?

_____

2   Do you play soccer well or badly?

_____

3   How often are you late for school?

_____

4   Who is the tallest in your class?

_____

Chapter

전치사

6

I can do it!

장소를 나타내는 전치사

in, under, on, behind

🌸 전치사는 명사나 대명사 앞에 놓여서 명사의 위치, 시간, 방향 등을 나타내요.

🌸 장소를 나타내는 전치사 1

in ~ 안에	under/below ~ 밑에	on ~ 위에	behind ~ 뒤에

The dog is **in** the box.   The dog is **on** the box.

The dog is **under** the chair.   The dog is **behind** the box.

Quick
Check-Up   Look and match.

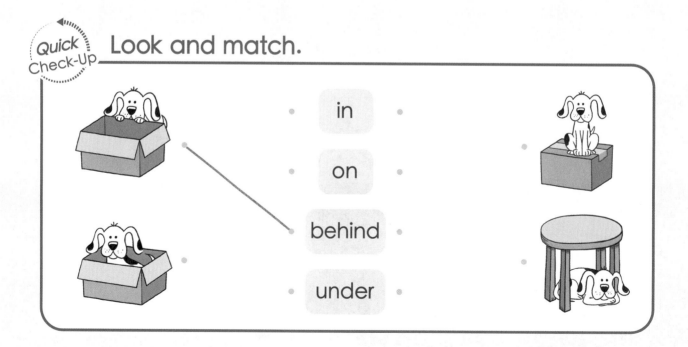

in

on

behind

under

in, under, on, behind

A Look, read, and write.

1. The book is ____on____ the desk.

2. The cats are _____ the table.

3. The slippers are _____ the desk.

4. The child is _____ the box.

in

on

under

behind

B Look, correct, and rewrite.

1. The dog is ~~in~~ the box.   ____behind____

2. The dog is **on** the box.   _____

3. The dog is **behind** the table.   _____

4. The dog is **under** the box.   _____

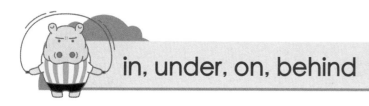

in, under, on, behind

 **Read and draw.**

1 This is my room.

2 The bag is on the bed.

3 The lamp is behind the chair.

4 The box is on the table.

장소를 나타내는 전치사

in front of, by, between

🌸 장소를 나타내는 전치사 2

in front of ~ 앞에	**next to/by/beside** ~ 옆에	**between** ~ 사이에

The dog is **in front of** the box.

The dog is **next to** the box.

The dog is **between** the boxes.

Quick Check-Up

Look and match.

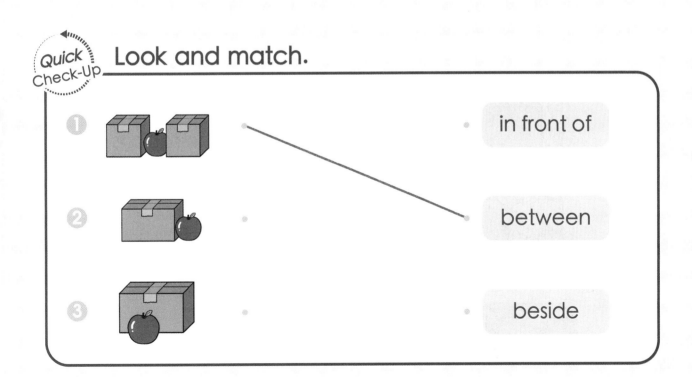

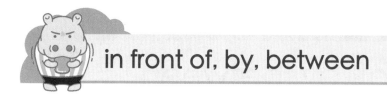 in front of, by, between

A Read and circle.

1

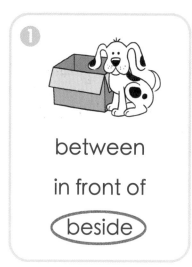

between

in front of

(beside)

2

under

between

in front of

3

behind

in front of

beside

B Look, read, and write.

in front of   between   beside

1 Where is the box?

- It is ___between___ the rabbits.

2 Where is the rabbit?

- It is _____ the box.

3 Where is the rabbit?

- It is _____ the box.

 Write the names of the children.

1. Sam is in front of the bushes.

2. A bag is between Suzy and Amy.

3. Mike is behind the bushes.

4. John is in the wooden house.

at, on, in

❀ 시간을 나타내는 전치사 1

at	구체적인 시각 앞에, 특정한 때	**at** 5 o'clock, **at** noon, **at** night
on	날짜, 요일 앞에, 특정한 때	**on** May 12, **on** Friday, **on** Christmas Day
in	긴 시간 앞에	**in** 2018, **in** June, **in** winter, **in** the morning

연도, 월, 계절, 오전, 오후 등을 나타낼 때 in을 써요.

Quick Check-Up Circle the correct ones.

① (at) / in 7 o'clock

② at / in summer

③ on / at Halloween Day

④ in / on Monday

⑤ at / in 1997

⑥ at / in night

⑦ on / in September 23

⑧ at / in winter

⑨ on / in July

⑩ at / in the morning

at, on, in

A Read and write.

at	on	in

1 My birthday is ___on___ August 8.

2 It's hot _____ summer.

3 The movie starts _____ 9 o'clock.

4 We go to church _____ Sundays.

5 I graduated from Harvard _____ 2018.

B Correct and rewrite.

1 I get up ~~in~~ 7 o'clock. ___at___

2 We invite them **in** Christmas Day. _____

3 She went to USA **on** 2017. _____

4 I get up **at** the morning. _____

5 Summer vacation starts **in** July 3. _____

6 I don't go to school **at** Saturdays. _____

at, on, in

 **Fun Wrap-Up!** Cut and put.

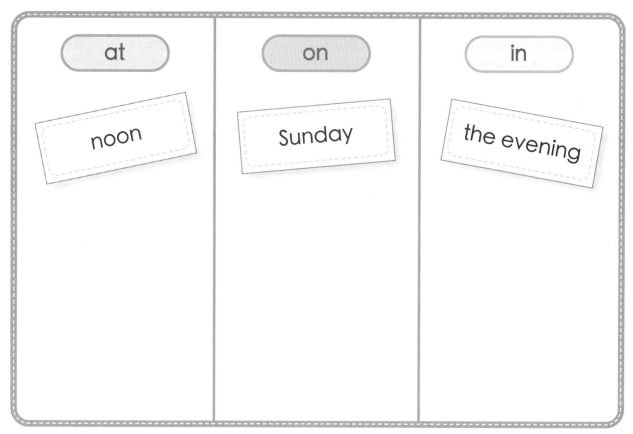

at	on	in
noon	Sunday	the evening

※ 아래와 동일한 카드가 159쪽에 있습니다. 해당 페이지의 카드를 사용하세요.

the evening	April	Sunday	2015
night	February	May 12	summer
Wednesday	the afternoon	Christmas Day	fall
06:00	noon	June	spring

Go to p. 159

Lesson 28

before, after, for, during

시간을 나타내는 전치사

🌼 시간을 나타내는 전치사 2

before	∼ 전에	I have to finish my homework **before** dinner.
after	∼ 후에	I brush my teeth **after** dinner. Spring comes **after** winter.
for	∼ 동안 (for+숫자)	She walks **for** 30 minutes. I wash my hands **for** 30 seconds.
during	∼ 동안 (during+특정 기간)	We visit my aunt **during** the summer vacation.

Circle the correct ones.

❶ I eat lunch 〉during / before〈 1 o'clock.

❷ We play soccer 〉during / for〈 2 hours.

❸ We are tired 〉in / (after)〈 the picnic.

❹ I fall asleep 〉during / for〈 the class.

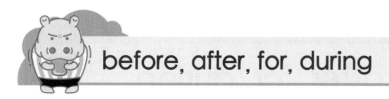

before, after, for, during

A Fill in the blanks.

before	after	during	for

① I read a book ____for____ 1 hour a day.

② I stay in England __d_____ the summer vacation.

③ He dries his body __a_____ shower.

④ I have to arrive at school __b_____ 9 o'clock.

B Read and circle.

① I go there { during / (before) } 10 p.m.

② He brushes his teeth { after / for } meals.

③ She washes her hands { before / for } 30 seconds.

④ Tom should go to sleep { during / before } 10 p.m.

 Cut and paste.

True? False?

① Summer comes after spring.

② Babies usually sleep for 12 hours.

③ People usually go to the beach during summer vacation.

④ Wednesday comes before Tuesday.

※ 아래와 동일한 카드가 159쪽에 있습니다. 해당 페이지의 카드를 사용하세요.

TRUE	FALSE	TRUE	FALSE
TRUE	FALSE	TRUE	FALSE

Go to p. 159

방향을 나타내는 전치사

up, down, into, out of

✿ 방향을 나타낼 때도 전치사를 사용해 표현해요.

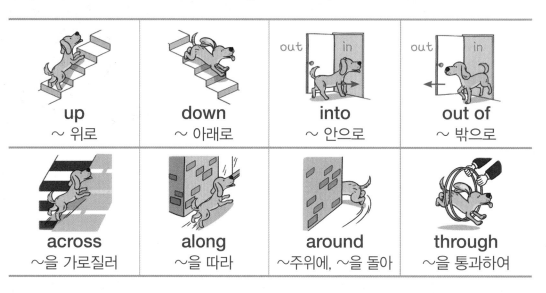

| up
~ 위로 | down
~ 아래로 | into
~ 안으로 | out of
~ 밖으로 |
| across
~을 가로질러 | along
~을 따라 | around
~주위에, ~을 돌아 | through
~을 통과하여 |

Walk **along** the trails.
Run **across** the road.

Turn **around** the corner.
Walk **down** the stairs.

Circle the correct *prepositions*.

• preposition 전치사

① The frog jumps (into)/ across the box.

② Jane swims over / across the river.

③ The girl turns along / around the corner.

④ The boy walks down / through the stairs.

up, down, into, out of

A Find and circle the *prepositions*.

A ball bounces (into) the box.
It bounces out of the box.
It rolls down the hill.
It rolls along the road.
Catch it.

B Look and match.

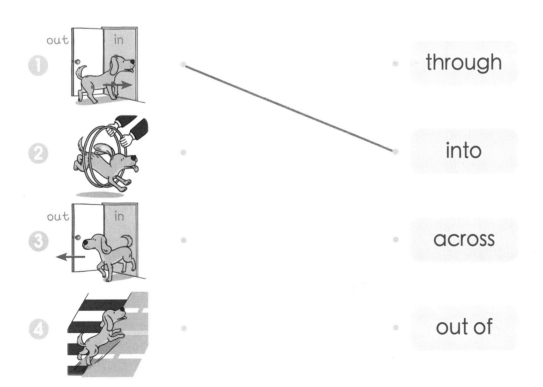

- through
- into
- across
- out of

up, down, into, out of

 Read and write.

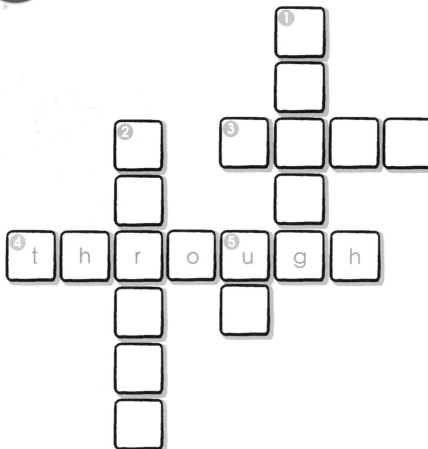

④ t h r o u g h

across

up

along

down

through

Down	**Across**

① A train goes _____ the railroad.

② A boy runs _____ the street.

⑤ They go _____ the stairs.

③ The truck goes _____ the hill.

④ She looks _____ the window.

방향을 나타내는 전치사

to, for

❋ to, for도 방향을 나타내는 전치사예요.

to	~ (쪽)으로	**to** the museum, **to** the station
for	~을 향해서, ~로 가는	**for** Seoul, **for** Japan

I go **to** the museum.

They leave **for** London.

목적지, 도착 지점 앞에 쓰이는
for는 동사 leave(떠나다),
head(향하다)와 많이 쓰여요.

Quick
Check-Up

Circle the correct ones.

❶ The bus is to / for Busan.

❷ The train is to / for Paris.

❸ She goes (to) / for the museum.

 **to, for**

A **Read and write.**

to	for

1. I go _____to_____ New York.

2. She comes _____ my office.

3. I must go _____ the north.

4. The airplane is leaving _____ Chicago.

5. The man runs _____ the school.

B **Write the right numbers in the correct box.**

1. The birds fly _____to_____ the south.

2. The girl leaves _____for_____ China.

3. Is this train _____ Seoul?

4. He runs _____ the station.

5. I go _____ the airport.

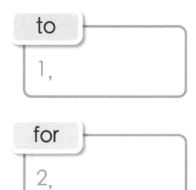

to
1,

for
2,

Follow and write.

The dog turns…

The bus leaves…

The girl goes…

The girl swims…

Busan

1

① around the corner.   ③ across the river.

② for Busan.   ④ to the museum.

There is, There are

긍정문

❀ There is ~, There are ~는 '~이 있다'라는 뜻이에요.
be동사 다음에 단수 명사나 셀 수 없는 명사가 오면 There is,
복수 명사가 오면 There are를 사용해요.

• There is+단수 명사/셀 수 없는 명사

There is a ball
on the table.

There is water
on the ground.

• There are+복수 명사

There are toys
in the box.

Quick Check-Up — Circle the correct ones.

① There is / are milk.

② There is / are cups.

③ There is / are a kid.

④ There is / are pencils.

⑤ There is / are an apple.

⑥ There is / are bread.

⑦ There is / are bags.

⑧ There is / are a chair.

⑨ There is / are an eraser.

⑩ There is / are rabbits.

긍정문

A Look and write.

	There is	There are

① <u>There is</u> a book on the bed.

② _____ pictures on the walls.

③ _____ a sock on the shelf.

④ _____ books on the shelf.

B Correct and rewrite.

① There ~~are~~ some bread.　　　There is some bread.

② There **is** five kids.　　　_____

③ There **is** cats in the box.　　　_____

④ There **are** a pen.　　　_____

⑤ There **are** some coffee.　　　_____

 Read and draw.

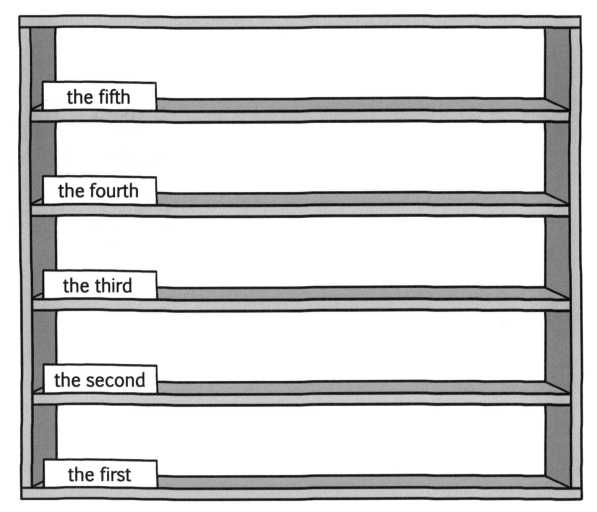

the fifth

the fourth

the third

the second

the first

① There are three cups on the first shelf.

② There are two erasers on the third shelf.

③ There are three toy cars on the fifth shelf.

④ There is a pen on the second shelf.

⑤ There is an apple on the fourth shelf.

There is, There are

부정문, 의문문

* There is/are 부정문은 is/are 뒤에 not을 넣어서 만들어요.

There isn't a ball in the box.   **There aren't** books on the desk.

* There is/are 의문문은 [Is/Are there ~?] 형태로 나타내요.

Is there a doll in the box?

– Yes, there is.

– No, there is not(=isn't).

Are there desks in the classroom?

– Yes, there are.

– No, there are not(=aren't).

Quick Check-Up — Check the right place for *not*.

① There ____ are __✓__ books ____ in the bookcase.

② There ____ is ____ a vase ____ on the desk.

③ There ____ is ____ a piece of pizza ____ on the table.

④ There ____ are ____ pears ____ on the plate.

A Write the correct numbers to answer the questions.

> ① Yes, there is.   ③ Yes, there are.
> ② No, there isn't.   ④ No, there aren't.

① Are there bananas? .... [3]

② Is there an apple? .... [ ]

③ Are there strawberries? .... [ ]

④ Is there a piece of cake? .... [ ]

⑤ Are there candies? .... [ ]

B Correct and rewrite.

① There **not is** my pillow on the bed.

  There is not my pillow on the bed.

② There **are not** his book under the bed.

  _____

③ Are **dolls there** on the shelf?

  _____

Fun Wrap-Up! Write *TRUE* or *FALSE*.

1. There are many books in the bookcase.   _FALSE_

2. There is not a dog on the floor.   _____

3. There is not a pillow on the couch.   _____

4. There is a clock on the walls.   _____

5. There is not a cat on the floor.   _____

A Choose the correct answers.

1 I get up _____ the morning.

　① at ② in ③ on

2 I get up _____ 7 o'clock.

　① on ② at ③ in

3 Summer vacation starts _____ July 3.

　① in ② on ③ at

4 The train is _____ Paris.

　① to ② for ③ down

5 The girl leaves _____ China.

　① for ② at ③ to

B Fill in the blanks.

between	in front of	under	in

1 The dog is _____ the box.

2 The rabbit is _____ the box.

3 The dog is _____ the table.

4 The box is _____ the rabbits.

C Unscramble the sentences.

1   there / Are / strawberries?

_____

2   is / a / There / on the table. / book

_____

3   cats / are / There / in the box.

_____

4   is / pillow / not / on the bed. / There / my

_____

D Answer the questions.

1   Where do you live?

_____

2   What time do you get up in the morning?

_____

3   What do you do before dinner?

_____

4   What do you usually do during summer vacation?

_____

Chapter

조동사

7

I can do it!

긍정문

❋ 조동사 can은 '~ 할 수 있다'의 의미이며 [can+동사원형]의 형태로 써요.

I **can swim** well.

He **can runs** fast.

❋ can은 be able to로 바꿔 쓸 수 있고 [be able to+동사원형]의 형태로 써요.

I **am able to read** English.

Sam **is able to plays** the piano.

Quick Check-Up — Circle the correct ones.

❶ John can ⎡ ride / rides ⎤ a bike.

❷ They ⎡ is / (are) ⎤ able to play tennis.

❸ Tom ⎡ are / is ⎤ able to ⎡ swimming / swim ⎤ .

❹ Obama can ⎡ plays / play ⎤ soccer well.

긍정문

A Unscramble the sentences.

1 can / Tom / play tennis.

<u>Tom can play tennis.</u>

2 am able to / I / read books.

_____

3 ski. / able to / I / am

_____

4 Mom / sing / well. / can

_____

B Correct and rewrite.

1 We can ~~goes~~ fishing.   <u>We can go fishing.</u>

2 She can **plays** the violin.   _____

3 I **are** able to swim.   _____

4 They **is** able to ski.   _____

 긍정문

 Read, circle, and number.

Write the correct numbers below the pictures.

_____ 1 _____ _____

❶ I am able to (painting / (paint)) pictures.

❷ I can (plays / play) the piano.

❸ I can (plays / play) soccer.

❹ I am able to (helps / help) sick people.

Can, Be able to 1

부정문

❈ can의 부정문은 can 뒤에 not을 써서 [can not+동사원형] 형태로 만들어요. can not은 cannot으로 붙여 쓰기도 하고 can't로 줄여 쓸 수도 있어요.

Sam **can not** swim.　　　　　Tom **can not** play tennis.
　　(=cannot / can't)　　　　　　　　(=cannot / can't)

❈ be able to의 부정문은 be동사 다음에 not을 써서
[be+not+able to+동사원형]으로 만들어요.

I **am not able to** fly.

You **are not able to** swim.

She **is not able to** speak English.

He **is not able to** ride a bike.

Quick Check-Up ── Circle the correct ones.

❶ Jane ⟨is not⟩/ am not　able to fly.

❷ They can not / not can　run fast.

❸ I am not / are not　able to read Chinese.

❹ He can't plays / play　soccer well.

❺ You not can / can't　ride a bike.

 부정문

A Unscramble the sentences.

1 He / is / not / make / able to / a desk.

   He is not able to make a desk.

2 not / I / am / drive a car. / able to

   _____

3 cannot / They / play tennis.

   _____

4 able to / I / read English. / not / am

   _____

B Choose and write.

can	not	able to	is

1 He ___can___ not run fast.

2 I am _____ able to speak Chinese.

3 She is not _____ play the piano.

4 Jenny _____ not able to play tennis.

Look and write.

can   can't

① Birds ___can___ fly, but they ___can't___ swim.

② Fish _____ swim, but they _____ run.

③ Rabbits _____ hop, but they _____ swim.

④ Turtles _____ walk fast, but they _____ swim.

⑤ Monkeys _____ ride a bike, but they _____ climb trees.

Can, Be able to 2

can 의문문

✿ can을 써서 '~ 할 수 있니?'라고 물을 때는 [Can+주어+동사원형 ~?]
형태로 질문해요. 긍정일 때는 [Yes, 주어+can.], 부정일 때는
[No, 주어+can not.]으로 답해요.

Can you jump high**?**   **Can** he swim**?**

– Yes, I can.   – Yes, he can.

– No, I can not.   – No, he can not.

  (=cannot / can't)   (=cannot / can't)

Quick Check-Up ___ Check the correct answers.

① Can he ride a bike?

☑ Yes, he can.

☐ No, he can't.

② Can he fly a kite?

☐ Yes, he can.

☐ No, he can't.

③ Can they play baseball?

☐ Yes, they can.

☐ No, they can't.

can 의문문

A Read and match.

1 Can you sing? •   • Yes, they can.

2 Can they go fishing? •   • No, I can't.

3 Can Suzy play the piano? •   • No, she can't.

4 Can he dance? •   • Yes, he can.

5 Can you read Chinese? •   • Yes, I can.

B Look and answer.

1 Can she swim?

- Yes, _____she can_____ .

2 Can they dance?

- Yes, _____ .

3 Can she draw a picture?

- Yes, _____ .

can 의문문

 Look, read, and answer.

Tom	✕	○	○	✕
Peter	○	✕	○	✕
James	○	✕	○	✕
Scott	✕	○	○	✕

① Can Tom play soccer?   -   No, he can't.

② Can Peter play tennis?   -

③ Can James ski?   -

④ Can Scott play the piano?   -

Can, Be able to 2

be able to 의문문

✿ be able to 의문문의 형태는 [be동사＋주어＋able to＋동사원형 ～?]
이고, 대답은 [Yes, 주어＋be동사.] 또는 [No, 주어＋be동사＋not.]
으로 해요.

Are you **able to** fly a kite**?**

– Yes, I am.

– No, I am not(=I'm not).

Is she **able to** play soccer**?**

– Yes, she is.

– No, she is not(=isn't).

Is Tom **able to** swim**?**

– Yes, he is.

– No, he is not(=isn't).

Are they **able to** play baseball**?**

– Yes, they are.

– No, they are not(=aren't).

Quick
Check-Up

Check the correct answers.

❶ Is he able to ride a bike?

☑ Yes, he is.

☐ Yes, he can.

❷ Is he able to fly a kite?

☐ Yes, he is.

☐ Yes, he can.

❸ Are they able to play baseball?

☐ Yes, they are.

☐ Yes, they can.

be able to 의문문

A Unscramble the sentences.

1. Is / able to / he / play the piano?

   Is he able to play the piano?

2. Are / able to / swim? / you

   _____

3. they / speak / English? / able to / Are

   _____

B Read and write.

is / Is	able to	isn't	No	are

1. __Is__ a bird able to fly?   - Yes, it __is__ .

2. Is he _____ play the violin?   - No, he _____ .

3. Are they _____ ski?   - _____, they aren't.

4. Are you able to run fast?   - Yes, we _____ .

 Write and color.

Yes, it is.   No, it isn't.

Is a bird able to fly? Yes, it is.	Is a cheetah able to run fast? _____	Is a rabbit able to hop? _____
Is a cat able to swim? _____	Is an elephant able to stomp? _____	Is a snake able to walk? _____
Is a horse able to drive a car? _____	Is a frog able to swim? _____	Is a mouse able to talk? _____

1 What letter did you make? _____

2 How many red boxes are there? _____

3 How many blue boxes are there? _____

Must, Have/Has to

긍정문

❀ must는 '~해야 한다'라는 뜻으로 강한 의무를 나타내요.
[must+동사원형]의 형태로 써요.
You **must** study hard.
He **must** do his homework.

❀ must는 have to로 바꿔 쓸 수 있어요.
주어가 3인칭 단수일 때에는 have to 대신 has to를 써요.
They **have to** brush their teeth.
She **has to** go to bed early.

Quick Check-Up — Circle the correct ones.

① He must ⟨work⟩/ works tonight.

② I have to / has to wash my hands.

③ She has to / have to tell the truth.

④ They must go / go must to school.

⑤ Tom has to brushes / brush his teeth.

⑥ He has to / have to go to bed early.

긍정문

A Choose and write.

must	have to	has to

① He __has__ __to__ wash his face.

② You _____ listen to your mom.

③ They _____ _____ keep the rules.

④ I _____ _____ share this bench.

⑤ She _____ _____ come home early.

B Read and circle.

① I must ⟨drink⟩/ drinks water every day.

② Sam have to / has to wear uniform.

③ They have to / has to follow the rules.

④ You must stop / stops before crossing roads.

⑤ Suzy have to / has to finish her work by 9 p.m.

 긍정문

 Color the footprints and make sentences.

| I | have to | eat | breakfast. |

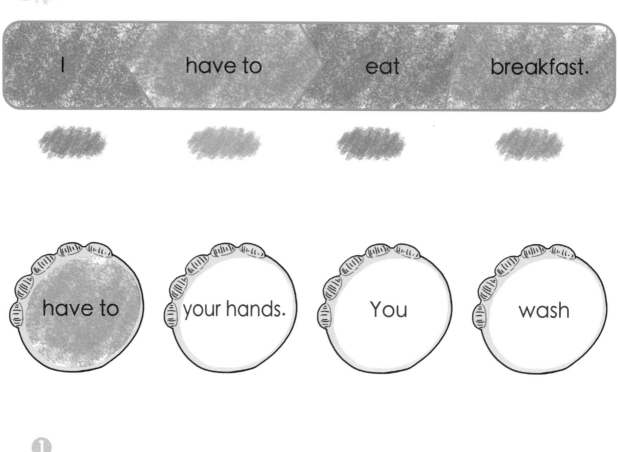

have to | your hands. | You | wash

① _____

practice | has to | He | tennis.

② _____

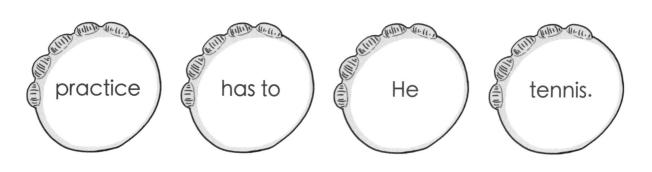

Lesson 33 — Must, Have/Has to

부정문

❀ must not은 '~하면 안 된다'라는 뜻으로 강한 금지를 나타내요. [must not+동사원형] 형태로 만들고, must not은 mustn't로 줄여 쓸 수 있어요. 하지만 mustnot으로 붙여 쓸 수는 없답니다.

You **must not** tease your friends. (○)
You **mustn't** tease your friends. (○)
You **mustnot** tease your friends. (×)

❀ [do/does+not+have to+동사원형]은 '꼭 ~할 필요는 없다'라는 의미로 의무는 아니라는 뜻이에요. don't/doesn't have to로 줄여 쓸 수 있어요.

I **don't have to** get up early.
She **doesn't have to** worry about it.

Quick Check-Up — Circle the correct ones.

❶ He | don't / (doesn't) | have to work weekends.

❷ We | mustnot / must not | run in the classroom.

❸ You | don't / doesn't | have to go fishing with me.

❹ You | mustn't / mustnot | touch this.

❺ We | don't / doesn't | have to go to bed early.

부정문

A Check the right place for *not*.

1. We _____ must __✓__ hit _____ other people.

2. You _____ must _____ make _____ a noise.

3. They _____ do _____ have to be here.

4. She _____ does _____ have to choose this.

B Read and match.

1. You must not run in the classroom.

2. We must not cry.

3. She must take care of her cat.

4. You don't have to read this book.

 Check the good children.

☑ Sam	☐ Suzy	☐ Tom
We must help each other.	You don't have to listen to your teacher.	You must not do your homework.
☐ Mike	☐ Minji	☐ John
We have to keep the rules.	We must run in the classroom.	You must not tease your friends.
☐ David	☐ Susan	☐ Max
We must not hit friends.	I have to take care of my pets.	You must not clean your room.

Write the names of the good children.

_____Sam_____ , _____ , _____

_____ , _____

Should, Had better

should

✿ 조동사 should: 의무나 충고를 나타내는 조동사로 [should+동사원형]
의 형태로 써요.

의무	～해야 한다	You **should** do your homework.
충고	～하는 것이 좋겠다	He **should** take a rest. You **should** listen to me.

✿ should의 부정문: '～하면 안 된다, ～하지 않는 것이 좋겠다'라는 뜻으로
[should+동사원형]의 형태로 써요.

You **should not**(=**shouldn't**) forget your passport.

You **should not**(=**shouldn't**) draw on the walls.

You **should not**(= **shouldn't**) tease your friends.

should not은
shouldn't로
줄일 수 있어요.

Quick Check-Up — Circle the correct ones.

❶ You [(should listen) / listen should] carefully.

❷ I [should wash / wash should] my hands.

❸ She should not [makes / make] a noise.

❹ We [shouldn't / shouldnot] waste money.

 **should**

A Choose and write.

should   shouldn't

1. My hands are dirty. I ___should___ wash my hands.

2. You look tired. You _____ take a rest.

3. He has a headache. He _____ go to hospital.

4. It is too hot. You _____ touch it.

B Correct and rewrite.

1. You should ~~are~~ nice to your friends.

   You should be nice to your friends.

2. Children **shouldnot** tell a lie.

   _____

3. Tom should not **wastes** water.

   _____

 should

 Fun Wrap-Up! Give your advice to the children.

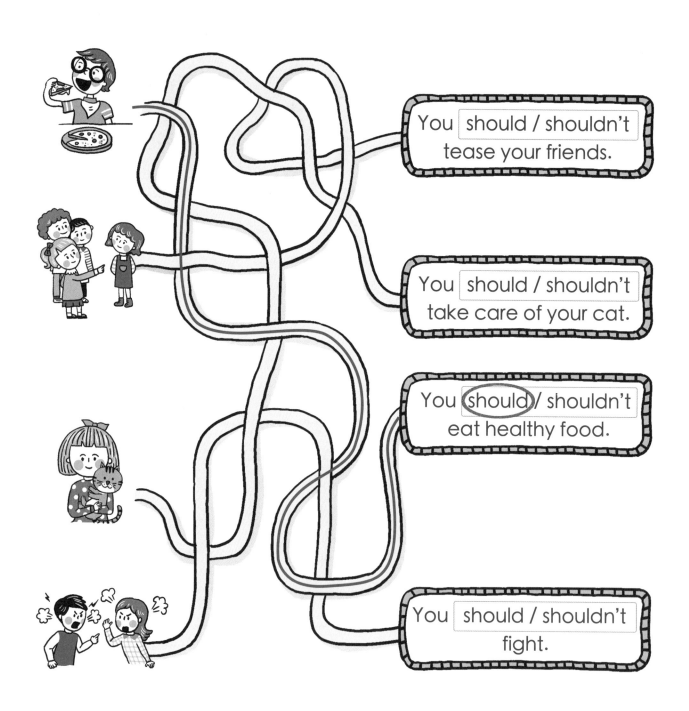

You should / shouldn't
tease your friends.

You should / shouldn't
take care of your cat.

You (should) / shouldn't
eat healthy food.

You should / shouldn't
fight.

had better

🌸 had better: 강한 권고를 나타내며 [had better+동사원형]의 형태로 써요. 부정문은 [had better not+동사원형]의 형태로 써요.

had better ~하는 것이 좋겠다	You **had better** (= You**'d better**) finish your work by tomorrow. She **had better** (= She**'d better**) stay with me.
had better not ~하지 않는 것이 좋겠다	You **had better not** stay with me. You**'d better not** run in the classroom. You **had better not** waste water. She**'d better not** drink coffee.

had better는
'd better로 줄여
쓸 수 있어요.

Quick
Check-Up

Circle the correct ones.

① had better call / had better to call

② had not better study / had better not study

③ had better get up / had better getting up

④ had not better eat / had better not eat

had better

A Read and write.

> had better   had better not

1. The train leaves in 5 minutes.

   You ____had better____ hurry up.

2. It's too noisy. You _____ make a noise.

3. It's cloudy. You _____ take an umbrella.

B Unscramble the sentences.

1. had better / do / You / your homework.

   You had better do your homework.

2. save / You / water. / had better

   _____

3. eat / You / junk food. / had better not

   _____

 Cut and paste.

① You had better drink water instead of coke.

②

③

※ 아래와 동일한 카드가 159쪽에 있습니다. 해당 페이지의 카드를 사용하세요.

| You had better not eat junk food. | You had better not watch TV too much. | You had better drink water instead of coke. |

Go to p. 159

Basic Test

A Choose the correct answers.

1　He _____ not run fast.

　　① able to　　　　　② can　　　　　③ not

2　She is not _____ play the piano.

　　① able　　　　　② able to　　　　　③ can

3　I am _____ able to speak Chinese.

　　① not　　　　　② can　　　　　③ cannot

4　She _____ come home early.

　　① have to　　　　　② has to　　　　　③ able to

5　He _____ work weekends.

　　① don't have to　　② doesn't have to　　③ don't has to

B Fill in the blanks.

had better	is not able to	must not	able to

1　I am _____ ski.

2　Jane _____ fly.

3　We _____ run in the classroom.

4　It's cloudy. You _____ take an umbrella.

C Unscramble the sentences.

1 can / can't / run. / swim, / Fish / but / they

_____

2 play / Scott / the / Can / piano?

_____

3 You / have to / go fishing / with me. / don't

_____

4 should / be / You / to / nice / your friends.

_____

D Answer the questions.

1 What can you do well?

_____

2 Are you able to speak English?

_____

3 What do you have to do every day?

_____

4 What should you do when you feel tired?

_____

Chapter

현재 시제

8

I can do it!

현재 시제의 쓰임

✿ 현재 시제는 '현재의 사실이나 상태'를 나타낼 때 사용하며, 항상 동사의 '현재형'으로 나타내요.

I **am** a student.　　　　　　　　He **works** in the hospital.

✿ 현재 시제는 다음과 같은 경우에 사용해요.

반복되는 일상·습관	I **go** to bed at 9.
일반적인 사실	Two plus three **is** five.
불변의 진리	The earth **moves** around the sun. The sun **rises** in the east.
속담·격언	There **is** no place like home. A friend in need **is** a friend indeed.

 Circle the correct ones.

① I ⓐm / is a teacher.

② You are / am my son.

③ My dad teaches / teach Korean.

④ He play / plays the piano every day.

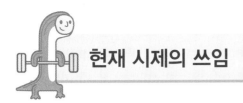 현재 시제의 쓰임

A Choose and match.

1. The bus _____ here.   had / have
2. They _____ every day.   stop / (stops)
3. Walls _____ ears.   teach / teaches
4. She _____ English.   exercise / exercises

B Correct and rewrite.

1. I ~~goes~~ to school at 8.   I go to school at 8.

2. She **eat** breakfast every morning.

   _____

3. I **has** two brothers. _____

4. The earth **moved** around the sun.

   _____

5. The sun **rose** in the east. _____

현재 시제의 쓰임

 Introduce your family.

My Family

I (am)/ is _____Jiho_____ .

This is / was my dad.

He is / are _____ .

This is / are my _____ .

She is / are _____ .

She like / likes _____ .

a student
~ years old
kind
nice
generous
strict
. . .

You can use these words.

Lesson
35

현재 시제 1

현재 시제 수 일치

❀ be동사의 현재형은 주어의 수와 인칭에 따라 모양이 바뀌어요.

수	인칭	주어	be동사	예문
단수	1인칭	I	am	I am(=I'm) Tom.
	2인칭	You	are	You are(=You're) kind.
	3인칭	He, She, It	is	He is(=He's) generous.
복수	1인칭	We	are	We are(=We're) in the room.
	2인칭	You	are	You are(=You're) my guests.
	3인칭	They	are	They are(=They're) cute.

❀ 일반동사 현재형: 주어가 <u>3인칭 단수</u>일 때는 -s/es를 붙여요.

→ He, She, It

I **like** English. → He **likes** English.
                        3인칭 단수

You **go** to school at 8. → She **goes** to school at 8.
                              3인칭 단수

Quick Check-Up

Check the correct ones.

☑ He likes apples.   ☐ We play in the park.

☐ I wash my hands.   ☐ They goes home.

☐ She speaks English.   ☐ He go shopping.

☐ It am cute.   ☐ David are happy.

현재 시제 수 일치

A Read, choose, and circle.

① Babies ⟨(cry) / cries⟩ at night.

③ They ⟨know / knows⟩ us.

② He ⟨play / plays⟩ baseball.

④ I ⟨study / studies⟩ hard.

B Look, read, and write.

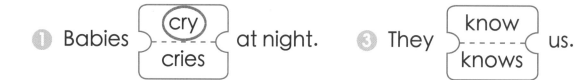

| fly | exercise | teach | miss | be |

① I ___fly___ a kite. She ___flies___ a kite.

② They ___miss___ you. He _____ you.

③ The teacher _____ math. They _____ math.

④ Tom _____ every day. We _____ every day.

⑤ I _____ in the room. They _____ in the kitchen.

⑥ She _____ happy. We _____ happy.

Find the way home.

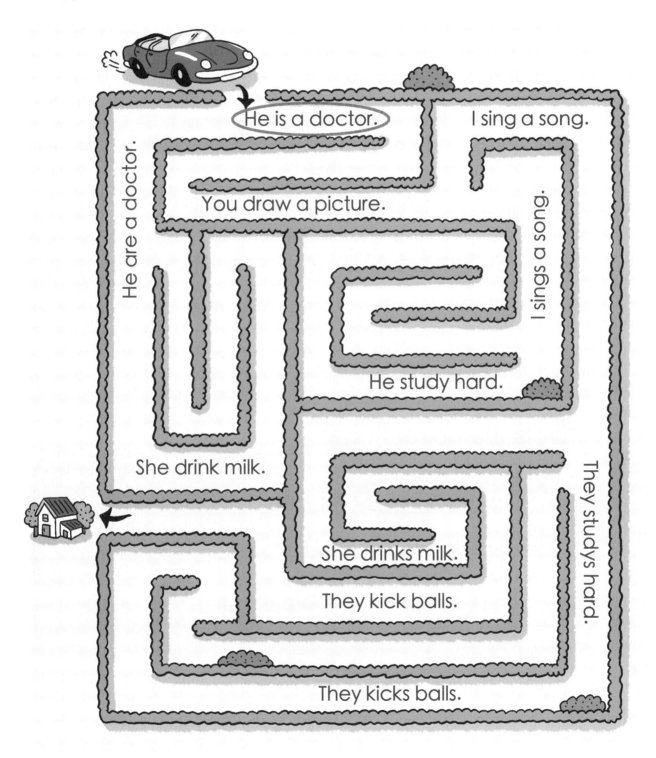

He is a doctor.

I sing a song.

He are a doctor.

You draw a picture.

I sings a song.

He study hard.

She drink milk.

They studys hard.

She drinks milk.

They kick balls.

They kicks balls.

Lesson

36

현재 시제 2

부정문

✿ be동사의 부정문은 [am/are/is+not]으로 나타내요.

I am hungry.　　　→ I **am not** hungry.

You are in London. → You **are not** in London.

She is happy.　　　→ She **is not** happy.

✿ 일반동사의 부정문은 [do/does+not+동사원형]으로 나타내요.
don't/doesn't로 줄여 쓸 수도 있어요.

I like vegetables.　→ I **do not**(=**don't**) **like** vegetables.

He likes meat.　　→ He **does not**(=**doesn't**) **like** meat.

Jane looks angry. → Jane **does not**(=**doesn't**) **look** angry.

Quick Check-Up

Circle the correct ones.

① Sara　do not /(does not) like math.

② He　do not / does not　study hard.

③ They　don't / doesn't　have breakfast.

④ I　am not / are not　10 years old.

⑤ We　don't / aren't　watch TV on Mondays.

부정문

A Unscramble the sentences.

1. does / She / not / smile.

   She does not smile.

2. a policeman. / is / He / not

   _____

3. wear / Sally / glasses. / not / does

   _____

B Write *do not* or *does not*.

do not	does not

1. She ___does not___ drink coffee.

2. Sam _____ look angry.

3. They _____ like games.

4. We _____ have dinner at school.

5. Nick and Sue _____ want to have a pet.

6. I _____ get up early.

 부정문

Look and write.

don't   doesn't   isn't   aren't

① Birds ___don't swim___, but they fly. (swim)

② A fish _____, but it swims. (run)

③ Rabbits _____ trees, but they hop. (climb)

④ A turtle _____, and it is slow. (fast)

⑤ Monkeys _____, but they climb trees. (fly)

⑥ Cows _____ meat, but they eat grass. (eat)

현재 시제 2

의문문

❋ be동사 현재 시제 의문문은 [Am/Are/Is＋주어 ～?] 형태로 만들고, 대답은 [Yes, 주어＋am/are/is.], [No, 주어＋am/are/is＋not.]으로 해요.

Are you busy**?**　　 – Yes, I am. / No, I'm not.

Is she old**?**　　 – Yes, she is. / No, she isn't.

Are they tired**?**　　 – Yes, they are. / No, they aren't.

❋ 일반동사의 의문문은 [Do/Does＋주어＋동사원형 ～?] 형태로 나타내고 대답은 [Yes, 주어＋do/does.], [No, 주어＋do/does not.]으로 해요.

Do you **like** reading books**?**　　 – Yes, I do. / No, I don't.

Does she **watch** TV**?**　　 – Yes, she does. / No, she doesn't.

Quick Check-Up

Circle the correct ones.

❶ (Do) / Are you play tennis?

❹ Does / Do he need them?

❷ Are / Do they students?

❺ Is / Does she 8 years old?

❸ Are / Is you angry?

❻ Does / Do he want a cat?

A Read and write.

| Am | Is | Do | Does |

1. ___Is___ your mom tall?

2. _____ I wrong?

3. _____ she get up early?

4. _____ we have homework today?

B Answer the questions.

1. Do they look happy?

   No, they don't.

2. Does he fly a kite?

   _____

3. Are you tired?

   _____

4. Is it rainy outside?

   _____

Make and say.

※ 아래와 동일한 전개도가 161쪽에 있습니다. 해당 페이지의 전개도를 사용하세요.

Do you have a pen?

Yes, I do.

you /
have a pen

lions /
eat carrots

David /
is smart

she /
have long
hair

they /
watch TV

Tom /
have a car

Roll the dice!
Ask and answer
the questions.

Go to p. 161

37

현재 진행형이란?

❀ '~하고 있는 중이다'라고 현재 진행 중인 일을 표현하고 싶을 때는 현재 진행형을 써요. 현재 진행형은 [am/are/is＋동사원형 -ing]로 나타내요.

I **am swimming**.

He **is reading** a book.

She **is running**.

They **are fighting** now.

Quick Check-Up Circle the correct ones.

① I (**am flying** / is flying) a kite.

② They (**are singing** / is singing) a song.

③ She (are kicking / **is kicking**) the ball.

④ The man (are standing / **is standing**) in a line.

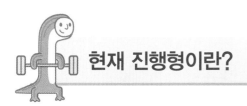

현재 진행형이란?

A Complete the *present continuous sentences*.

① I __am taking__ a rest now. (take)

② She _____ a piece of pizza now. (eat)

③ He _____ soccer. (play)

④ The sun _____. (shine)

B Correct and rewrite in the *present continuous form*.

① He ~~studying~~ math hard.   He is studying math hard.

② I **am make** a cake now.   _____

③ She **washing** her hands.   _____

④ They **is waiting** for a bus.   _____

⑤ The dog **is bark**.   _____

현재 진행형이란?

 Fun Wrap-Up! Follow the correct sentences.

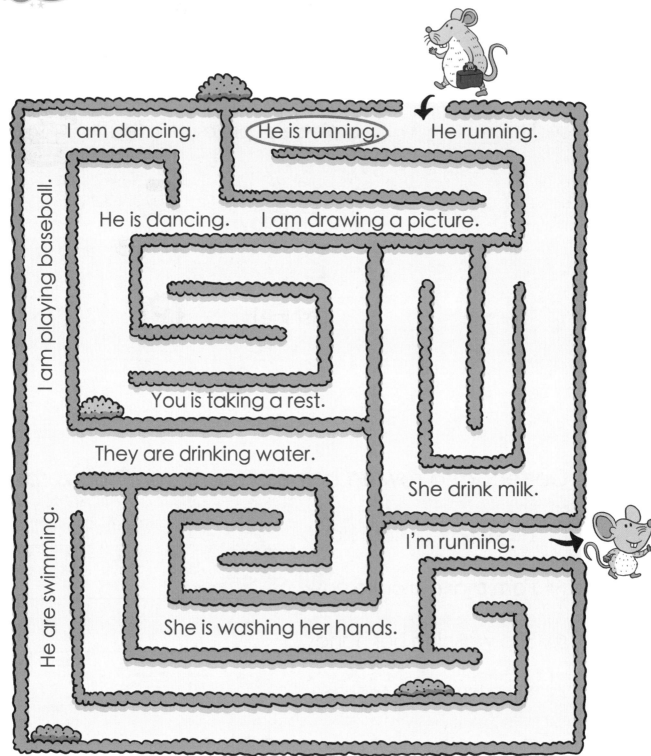

I am dancing.   He is running.   He running.

I am playing baseball.

He is dancing.   I am drawing a picture.

You is taking a rest.

They are drinking water.

She drink milk.

He are swimming.

I'm running.

She is washing her hands.

현재 진행형 vs 단순 현재

✿ '소유, 감정, 감각, 인식' 등을 나타내는 <u>상태동사</u>들은 진행형으로 잘 쓰지 않아요.

소유	have	want	need
감정	like	love	hate
감각	see	smell	hear
인식	know	believe	forget

I **have** a pencil. (O)   I'**m having** a pencil. (X)

✿ 현재 시제는 '현재의 습관이나 사실, 반복적으로 일어나는 일'을 나타내고, 현재 진행형은 '바로 지금 진행 중'인 일을 나타내요.

She **is** a teacher. (현재 시제)

She **is teaching** English. (현재 진행형)

have가 '먹다'라는 뜻으로 사용될 땐 진행형으로 쓸 수 있어요.

Quick Check-Up — ## Check the correct ones.

☐ He is having a car.   ☑ We are running.

☐ She is speaking Chinese.   ☐ I am washing my hands.

☐ You are driving now.   ☐ They are going home.

☐ He is needing a book.   ☐ He is believing it.

A Read and circle.

1. He (needs / is needing) to sleep.

2. I have / am having a flower.

3. Jane likes / is liking apples.

4. They want / are wanting a big house.

5. We hate / are hating each other.

B Write the sentences in the *present simple* or the *present continuous form*.

1. Sam _____knows_____ you. (know)

2. Jane _____ on the phone now. (talk)

3. Dad _____ dinner now. (cook)

4. They _____ their friends now. (help)

5. He _____ in God. (believe)

6. We _____ to music now. (listen)

 Complete the puzzle.

d r i v i n g

Lesson 37 113

Down

① He is _____ pasta now.
   (cook)

② She _____ in New York.
   (live)

③ It _____ good.
   (smell)

Across

④ He is _____ a car now.
   (drive)

⑤ We _____ eating apples.
   (be)

⑥ She _____ cats.
   (like)

현재 진행형 형태 (1)

🌸 현재 진행형을 만들 때 대부분의 동사는 동사원형에 -ing를 붙여요.

eat	→ eat**ing**	go	→ go**ing**	walk	→ walk**ing**
fly	→ fly**ing**	cook	→ cook**ing**	water	→ water**ing**
wash	→ wash**ing**	study	→ study**ing**		

She is **watering** the flowers.　　I am **studying** math.

🌸 e로 끝나는 동사: e를 빼고 -ing를 붙여요.

write	→ writ**ing**	make	→ mak**ing**	come	→ com**ing**
take	→ tak**ing**	smile	→ smil**ing**	give	→ giv**ing**
dance	→ danc**ing**	have	→ hav**ing**		

I am **having** lunch.　　　　They are **dancing**.

Quick Check-Up

Check the correct ones.

☑ She is making a chair.　　☐ I am watering the plants.

☐ They are danceing.　　　☐ We are coming!

☐ I am going to the zoo.　　☐ I am flying a kite.

☐ Mom is haveing lunch.　　☐ She is studing math.

☐ Dad is cooking supper.　　☐ They are walking.

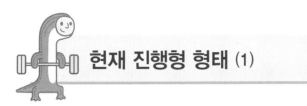 현재 진행형 형태 (1)

A Read, choose, and match.

1. I am ⟨reading⟩ / read a book.

2. She is walking / walkking .

3. They are dancing / danceing .

4. The train is runing / running .

B Complete the *present continuous sentences*.

1. She __is__ __making__ a sandcastle now. (make)

2. We _____ _____ the garden. (water)

3. They _____ _____ English. (study)

4. The man _____ _____ to me. (come)

5. Sam _____ _____ his car. (park)

 Write the *present continuous forms* of the verbs.

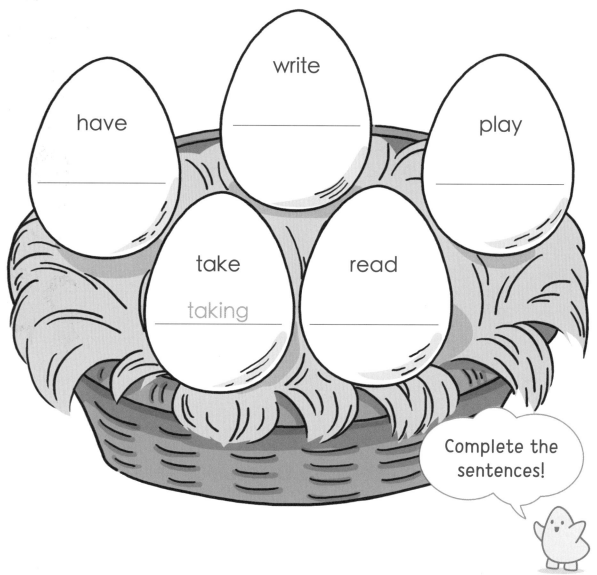

Complete the sentences!

1 <u>I am taking pictures.</u>

2 We _____ tennis.

3 They _____ breakfast.

4 I _____ a letter.

5 He _____ a book.

현재 진행형 형태 (2)

❀ ie로 끝나는 동사

lie → l**ying**   die → d**ying**

She is **lying** on the grass.   The flower is **dying**.

❀ [단모음＋단자음]으로 끝나는 동사

put → put**ting**   run → run**ning**   sit → sit**ting**
stop → stop**ping**

Jim is **putting** down his bag.   I am **stopping** my car.

They are **running**.   Mom is **sitting** on a chair.

Quick
Check-Up ── Check the correct ones.

☑ They are running.   ☐ She is lieing on the bed.

☐ He is lying on the grass.   ☐ He is runing.

☐ The car is stoping.   ☐ He is siting on a sofa.

☐ I am sitting on a bench.   ☐ My flower is dying.

☐ They are putting the books on the desk.

A Read and circle.

1 The man is (**putting** / puting) his jacket on the chair.

2 They are (sitting / siting) on the bench.

3 She is (chatting / chating) with her friend.

B Complete the *present continuous sentences.*

run	cut	sit	swim	lie

1 My dad ___is___ ___sitting___ on the sofa.

2 Max _____ __r_____ with his friends.

3 John _____ ___l_____ on the bed.

4 He _____ ___c_____ the paper.

5 We _____ ___s_____ in the river.

 Read and color.

right ones
wrong ones

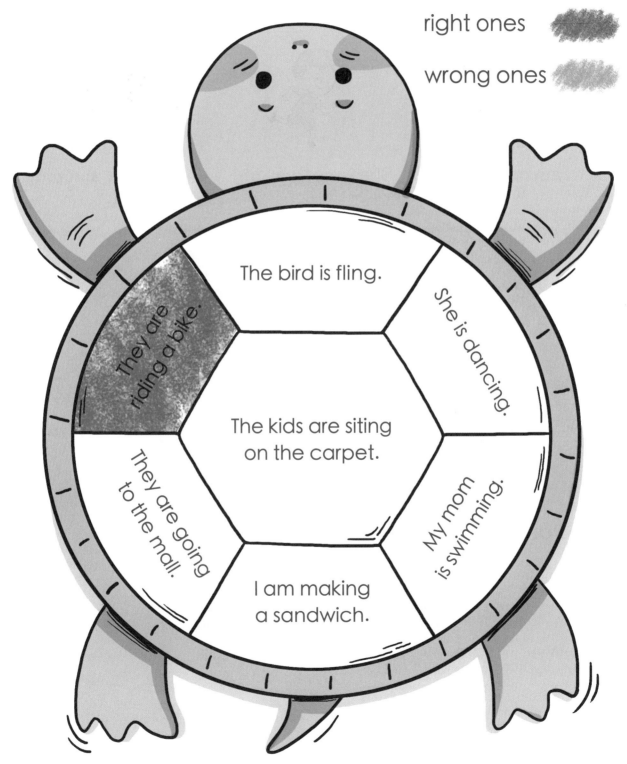

The bird is fling.

She is dancing.

They are riding a bike.

The kids are siting on the carpet.

They are going to the mall.

My mom is swimming.

I am making a sandwich.

부정문

❀ 현재 진행형의 부정문은 현재 '~을 하고 있지 않다'라고 말할 때 사용하며 [be동사+not+동사원형-ing] 형태로 써요.

I am not standing.

She is not walking.

We are not sleeping on the sofa.

Quick Check-Up — ## Check the right place for *not*.

❶ I ___ am ✔ looking at the monkeys.

❷ Paul ___ is ___ walking on the road.

❸ They ___ are ___ watching TV in the room.

❹ We ___ are ___ painting on the walls.

❺ She ___ is ___ talking ___ on the phone.

부정문

A Read and choose.

1. You are not walking / not are walking on the road.
   (are not walking is circled)

2. I am not studying / am studying not math now.

3. Children not are watching / are not watching TV.

4. Evan is not reading / is reading not a comic book.

5. I not am dancing / am not dancing here.

B Complete the sentences in the *negative form*.

1. Mom __is not packing__ her lunch. (pack)

2. He is _____ the guitar. (play)

3. They are _____ letters. (write)

4. I am _____ my hands. (wash)

5. David is _____ his homework. (do)

부정문

 Look and write.

1 Dad ____is not____ watching TV.

He is cooking lunch.

2 Mom _____ cooking lunch.

She is reading a book.

3 Grandma _____ having a meal.

She is drinking a cup of coffee.

부정문 줄임말

✿ 현재 진행형의 부정문은 아래와 같이 두 가지 형태로 줄일 수 있어요.

		줄임말 (1)	줄임말 (2)	
단수	I **am not**	I'**m** not	X	eating
	You **are not**	You'**re** not	You **aren't**	cooking
	He **is not** She **is not** It **is not**	He'**s** not She'**s** not It'**s** not	He **isn't** She **isn't** It **isn't**	reading dancing writing
복수	We **are not** You **are not** They **are not**	We'**re** not You'**re** not They'**re** not	We **aren't** You **aren't** They **aren't**	coming running sitting

or +

She **is not** reading a book. → She'**s not** reading a book.

→ She **isn't** reading a book.

Quick Check-Up Circle the correct ones.

❶ (You're not) / You isn't taking a shower.

❷ They aren't / They're aren't having breakfast.

❸ She aren't / She's not cleaning her room.

부정문 줄임말

A Unscramble the sentences.

① not / She's / cooking / pasta.

She's not cooking pasta.

② working / not / on the computer. / He's

③ Grandpa. / We're / visiting / not

④ riding / not / I'm / a bike.

B Change the sentences like the example.

ex He is not studying. ➡ He isn't studying.

① You are not drawing cars. ➡ You aren't drawing cars.

② He is not driving a car. ➡

③ She is not taking pictures. ➡

④ I am not taking a bus. ➡

Look and match.

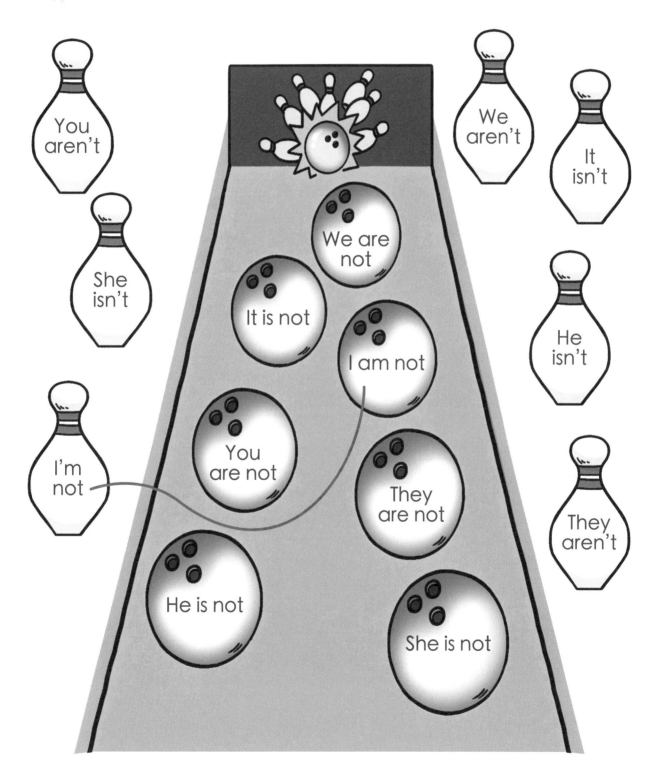

You aren't

She isn't

I'm not

We are not

It is not

I am not

You are not

They are not

He is not

She is not

We aren't

It isn't

He isn't

They aren't

현재 진행형: 의문문

질문하기

✿ '지금 무엇을 하고 있는지' 물을 때는 현재 진행형 의문문을 사용해요.
형태는 [be동사+주어+동사원형-ing ～?]로 나타내요.

Are you studying hard?

Is she singing a song?

Are they watching TV?

Is he sitting on a bench?

Quick Check-Up

Check the correct ones.

❶ ☐ Are you watching TV?

☐ Are you watch TV?

❷ ☐ Is he sing a song?

☐ Is he singing a song?

❸ ☐ Does she studying hard?

☐ Is she studying hard?

질문하기

A Change the sentences into the *questions*.

1. You are having dinner.   ○ <u>Are you having dinner</u> ?

2. He is cleaning his room.   ○ _____ ?

3. They are going to the market.

   ○ _____ ?

4. Tom is playing with blocks.

   ○ _____ ?

5. She is taking a nap.   ○ _____ ?

B Make the *present continuous questions*.

1. <u>Are you playing</u> the guitar? (you, play)

2. _____ on this project? (he, work)

3. _____ TV? (she, watch)

4. _____ basketball? (they, play)

5. _____ with Nancy? (Jimmy, dance)

6. _____ English? (you, study)

 Fun Wrap-Up!

Cut, paste, and write.

They are playing with a ball.

➡ _____ ?

※ 아래와 동일한 카드가 161쪽에 있습니다. 해당 페이지의 카드를 사용하세요.

Go to p. 161

현재 진행형: 의문문

대답하기

❋ 현재 진행형 의문문에는 다음과 같이 대답해요.

현재 진행형 의문문		긍정 대답	부정 대답
Are you studying math?		Yes, I am.	No, I'm not.
Is Suzan singing a song?		Yes, she is.	No, she isn't.

Quick Check-Up

Check the correct answers.

❶ Is he reading a book?

☑ Yes, he is.
☐ No, he isn't.

❷ Are they swimming?

☐ Yes, they are.
☐ No, they aren't.

❸ Are you playing tennis?

☐ Yes, I am.
☐ No, I'm not.

A Write the correct answers.

1. Are you learning Japanese? — Yes, _____I am_____ .

2. Are you dancing? — No, _____ .

3. Are you eating snacks? — Yes, _____ .

4. Is the cat sleeping? — No, _____ .

5. Is he taking a shower? — Yes, _____ .

B Write the words to make the correct sentences.

am	are / Are	aren't	is / Is	isn't

1. ___Are___ you reading a book? — Yes, I ___am___ .

2. _____ they jumping? — Yes, they _____ .

3. _____ she thinking about it? — No, she _____ .

4. _____ they moving the desk? — No, they _____ .

Fun Wrap-Up! Look and answer.

My Family

1. Is Dad watching TV? — _No, he isn't._

2. Is Mom reading a book? — _____

3. Is Grandma having a meal? — _____

4. Is Grandpa sleeping? — _____

A Choose the correct answers.

1 Sara _____ like math.
① does not ② do not ③ is not

2 They _____ have breakfast.
① doesn't ② don't ③ aren't

3 John is _____ on the bed.
① lieng ② lying ③ lieing

4 He _____ math hard.
① are studying ② is studying ③ am studying

5 They _____ for a bus.
① are waiting ② am waiting ③ is waiting

B Fill in the blanks.

| moves | now | having | barking |

1 The dog is _____.

2 Are you _____ dinner?

3 Jane is talking on the phone _____.

4 The earth _____ around the sun.

C Unscramble the sentences.

1   breakfast / She / every morning. / eats

_____

2   it / rainy / Is / outside?

_____

3   a bench. / I / sitting / on / am

_____

4   not / on the computer. / working / He's

_____

D Answer the questions.

1   Is it sunny outside?

_____

2   What time do you go to school?

_____

3   Are you watching TV now?

_____

4   What are you doing now?

_____

MEMO

2

Answers

부사의 역할

p. 6

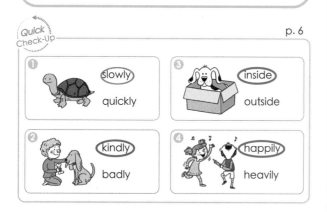

Quick Check-Up

① slowly / quickly

② kindly / badly

③ inside / outside

④ happily / heavily

A
p. 7

① I ate pizza (slowly).

② I make a card (easily).

③ He speaks (quietly).

④ I have (only) two pencils.

⑤ See you (later).

⑥ You speak English (well).

⑦ She comes (late).

⑧ The bird sings (beautifully).

B
p. 7

① Jack runs ___fast___ .   (fast) / slow

② She is ___very___ pretty.   here / (very)

③ The kids talk ___loudly___ .   (loudly) / up

④ Ann works ___hard___ .   really / (hard)

⑤ He gets up ___early___ .   (early) / down

⑥ I go to bed ___late___ .   (late) / up

Fun Wrap-Up!   p. 8

study hard · very beautiful · (study hard) · walk fastly · very pretty · study hard · eat fast · run fast · walk slowly · sing happily · pretty very · speak kindly · swim good · work hard · dance well

---

부사의 위치

p. 9

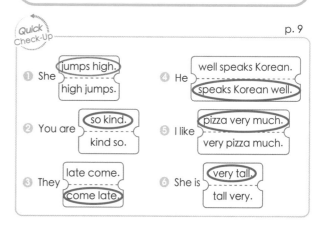

Quick Check-Up

① She — (jumps high.) / high jumps.

② You are — (so kind.) / kind so.

③ They — late come. / (come late)

④ He — well speaks Korean. / (speaks Korean well.)

⑤ I like — (pizza very much.) / very pizza much.

⑥ She is — (very tall.) / tall very.

A
p. 10

① Mom walks ___slowly___ .   slow / (slowly)

② These are ___very___ interesting.   (very) / hard

③ The students speak ___loudly___ .   (loudly) / very

④ We read it ___quickly___ .   (quickly) / very

⑤ Birds sing ___happily___ .   (happily) / so

B
p. 10

① run / The boys / fast.   The boys run fast.

② He / very / hard. / studies   He studies very hard.

③ milk / I / very much. / like   I like milk very much.

④ Tom / hard. / studies English   Tom studies English hard.

⑤ hop / Frogs / high.   Frogs hop high.

Answers vary.

Fun Wrap-Up!   p. 11

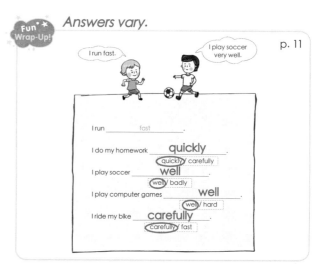

I run fast.   I play soccer very well.

I run ___fast___ .

I do my homework ___quickly___ .   (quickly) / carefully

I play soccer ___well___ .   (well) / badly

I play computer games ___well___ .   (well) / hard

I ride my bike ___carefully___ .   (carefully) / fast

Lesson 23 부사 2

부사의 형태: 규칙형

Quick Check-Up p. 12

① (gently) / gentlely
② busyly / (busily)
③ (slowly) / slowy
④ queity / (quietly)
⑤ happyly / (happily)
⑥ kindily / (kindly)
⑦ (simply) / simplely
⑧ (merrily) / merryly

A p. 13

① good — well
② correct — correctly
③ quiet — quietly
④ careful — carefully
⑤ simple — simply

B p. 13

Turtles walk (slowly).
Frogs jump (high).
Cheetahs run (fast).
Birds sing (happily).
I see the animals (carefully).

high   slowly   fast
happily   carefully

Fun Wrap-Up! p. 14

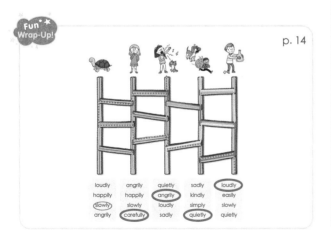

loudly / happily / (slowly) / angrily
angrily / happily / slowly / (carefully)
quietly / (angrily) / loudly / sadly
sadly / kindly / simply / (quietly)
(loudly) / easily / slowly / quietly

부사의 형태: 불규칙형

Quick Check-Up p. 15

① I get up (late) / lately in the morning.
② He works (hard) / hardly.
③ The dog runs (fast) / fastly.
④ Come (close) / closely.
⑤ I jump (high) / highly.

A p. 16

① I am a fast runner. → I run _fast_.
② He is a careful driver. → He drives _carefully_.
③ She is a slow swimmer. → She swims _slowly_.
④ He is a kind teacher. → He teaches _kindly_.
⑤ You are a hard worker. → You work _hard_.

B p. 16

① She drives her car careful. — carefully
② The car moves slow. — slowly
③ John plays football very good. — well
④ The team plays tennis bad. — badly
⑤ They run fastly. — fast

Fun Wrap-Up! p. 17

Lesson 24 빈도부사

빈도부사의 종류

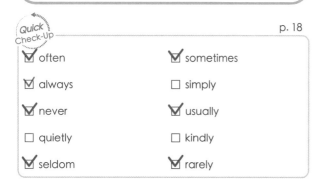

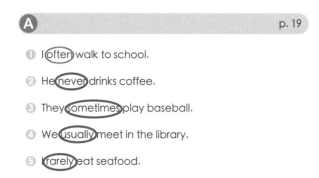

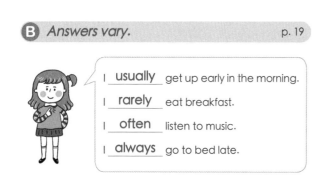

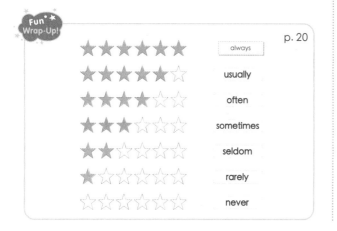

빈도부사의 위치

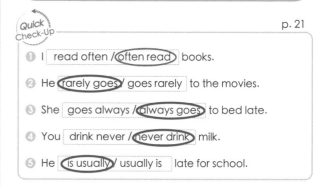

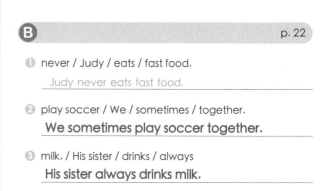

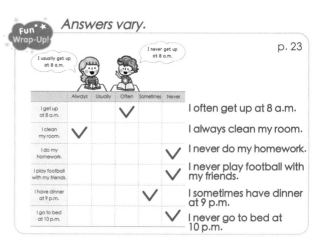

Lesson 25 형용사 비교급

형용사-er

Quick Check-Up p. 24

☑ short – shorter ☑ old – older

☑ smart – smarter ☑ young – younger

☐ small – more small ☑ deep – deeper

☐ tall – more tall ☐ famous – famouser

☑ beautiful – more beautiful ☐ difficult – difficulter

A p. 25

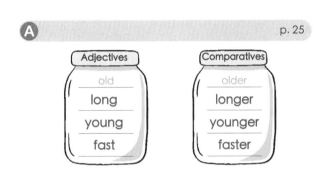

Adjectives	Comparatives
old	older
long	longer
young	younger
fast	faster

B p. 25

① tall – taller

③ slow – **slower**

② long – **longer**

④ old – **older**

Fun Wrap-Up! p. 26

The monkey is big. | The elephant is bigger.

The cat is tall. | **The dog is taller.**

The mouse is fast. | **The car is faster.**

형용사-er+than, more+형용사+than

Quick Check-Up p. 27

① biger /(bigger) ⑤ fater /(fatter)

② easyer /(easier) ⑥ happyer /(happier)

③ (older)/ oldder ⑦ hoter /(hotter)

④ importanter /(more important)

A p. 28

① bigger / The horse / the dog. / is / than
The horse is bigger than the dog.

② than / My sister / younger / Jane. / is
My sister is younger than Jane.

③ Summer / hotter / is / spring. / than
Summer is hotter than spring.

④ more important / This / than / is / that.
This is more important than that.

B p. 28

① Math is ~~difficulter~~ than science. more difficult

② Suzy is ~~more smart~~ than Tom. smarter

③ My room is ~~cleanner~~ than yours. cleaner

④ Dancing is ~~funnyer~~ than singing. funnier

Fun Wrap-Up! p. 29

	John	Judy	Suzy	Tom
	50 years old	45 years old	7 years old	10 years old
	170 cm	160 cm	100 cm	130 cm
	80 kg	60 kg	17 kg	30 kg

① John is older than Judy. (old)

② Suzy is **younger** than Tom. (young)

③ John is **taller** than Suzy. (tall)

④ Suzy is **happier** than Tom. (happy)

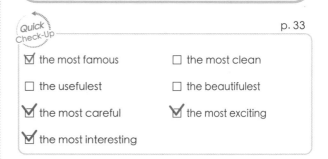

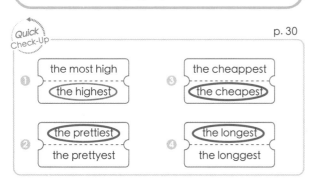

형용사 최상급

형용사-est

p. 30

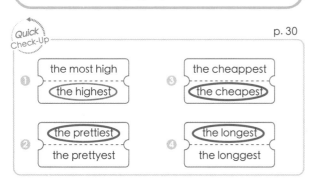

A
p. 31

1. girl / Mary / is / the bravest / in my class.
   Mary is the bravest girl in my class.

2. in my school. / the tallest / Paul / is
   Paul is the tallest in my school.

3. The bag / the cheapest / is / in the shop.
   The bag is the cheapest in the shop.

B
p. 31

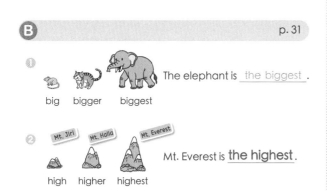

The elephant is the biggest.

Mt. Everest is the highest.

Fun Wrap-Up!
Answers vary.
In My Class
p. 32

① Who is the tallest student in your class?
   Minsu is the tallest student in my class.
② Who is the shortest student in your class?
   Sally is the shortest student in my class.
③ Who is the strongest student in your class?
   Jihoo is the strongest student in my class.
④ Who has the longest hair in your class?
   Jessica has the longest hair in my class.
⑤ Who has the biggest eyes in your class?
   Annie has the biggest eyes in my class.

the most+형용사

p. 33

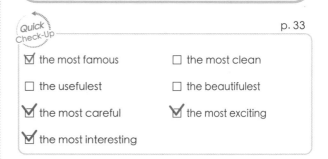

☑ the most famous ☐ the most clean
☐ the usefulest ☐ the beautifulest
☑ the most careful ☑ the most exciting
☑ the most interesting

A
p. 34

1. is / Science / most / the / difficult / subject.
   Science is the most difficult subject.

2. beautiful / My house / the / most / is / in the town.
   My house is the most beautiful in the town.

3. in the store. / This bag / expensive / the / is / most
   This bag is the most expensive in the store.

B
p. 34

① February is the shortest month of the year. (short)
② Horse riding is the most dangerous sport. (dangerous)
③ Tommy is the most popular in the school. (popular)
④ Star Wars is the most exciting in the world. (exciting)
⑤ This building is the highest in the town. (high)

Fun Wrap-Up!
p. 35

Quiz!
Mary is more intelligent than Suzy.
Mary is more intelligent than Judy.
Who is the most intelligent? Mary

Quiz!
Harry Potter is more interesting than Star Wars.
Star Wars is more interesting than Minions.
What is the most interesting? Harry Potter

Quiz!
Science is more difficult than English.
Math is more difficult than science.
What is the most difficult? Math

Basic Test

A
p. 36

1 I eat _____.
   ① fast　　　　② hungry　　　　③ happy

2 The boys _____.
   ① running fast　　② fast run　　③ run fast

3 He is a careful driver. → He drives _____.
   ① care　　② carefully　　③ be careful

4 Math is _____ than science.
   ① difficulter　　② more difficult　　③ difficult

5 The horse is _____ than the dog.
   ① bigger　　　　② big　　　　③ more big

B
p. 36

1 Turtles walk _____slowly_____.

2 This is _____very_____ hot.

3 Horse riding is the _____most_____ dangerous sport.

4 John is older _____than_____ Judy.

C
p. 37

1 You / too / are / young.
   You are too young.

2 play / I / soccer. / sometimes
   I sometimes play soccer.

3 Airplanes / faster / are / buses. / than
   Airplanes are faster than buses.

4 is / The car / the most / in the world. / expensive
   The car is the most expensive in the world.

D Answers vary.
p. 37

1 Do you eat fast or slowly?
   I eat slowly.

2 Do you play soccer well or badly?
   I play soccer well.

3 How often are you late for school?
   I am never late for school.

4 Who is the tallest in your class?
   Minsu is the tallest in my class.

in, under, on, behind

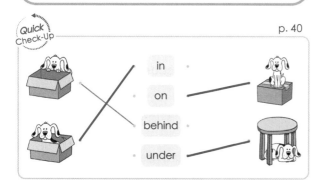

Quick Check-Up   p. 40

A   p. 41

1. The book is ___on___ the desk.
2. The cats are __under__ the table.
3. The slippers are __behind__ the desk.
4. The child is ___in___ the box.

B   p. 41

1. The dog is ~~in~~ the box.   behind
2. The dog is ~~on~~ the box.   in
3. The dog is ~~behind~~ the table.   under
4. The dog is ~~under~~ the box.   on

Answers vary.

Fun Wrap-Up!   p. 42

in front of, by, between

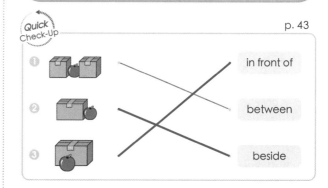

Quick Check-Up   p. 43

1 — between
2 — in front of
3 — beside

A   p. 44

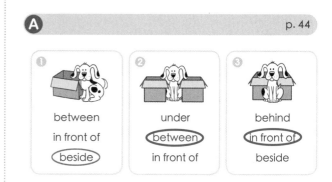

1. between / in front of / (beside)
2. under / (between) / in front of
3. behind / (in front of) / beside

B   p. 44

1. Where is the box?
   - It is __between__ the rabbits.
2. Where is the rabbit?
   - It is __in front of__ the box.
3. Where is the rabbit?
   - It is __beside__ the box.

Fun Wrap-Up!   p. 45

John
Mike
Amy
Suzy
Sam

at, on, in

① (at)/ in 7 o'clock

② at / (in) summer

③ (on)/ at Halloween Day

④ in / (on) Monday

⑤ at / (in) 1997

⑥ (at)/ in night

⑦ (on)/ in September 23

⑧ at / (in) winter

⑨ on / (in) July

⑩ at / (in) the morning

Ⓐ
p. 47

① My birthday is ___on___ August 8.

② It's hot ___in___ summer.

③ The movie starts ___at___ 9 o'clock.

④ We go to church ___on___ Sundays.

⑤ I graduated from Harvard ___in___ 2018.

Ⓑ
p. 47

① I get up ~~in~~ 7 o'clock.   at

② We invite them ~~in~~ Christmas Day.   on

③ She went to USA ~~on~~ 2017.   in

④ I get up ~~at~~ the morning.   in

⑤ Summer vacation starts ~~in~~ July 3.   on

⑥ I don't go to school ~~at~~ Saturdays.   on

at	on	in
noon	Sunday	the evening
night	May 12	April / 2015
06:00	Wednesday	February / summer
	Christmas Day	the afternoon / fall
		June / spring

before, after, for, during

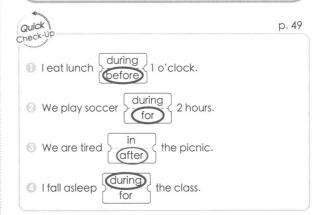

① I eat lunch } during / (before) { 1 o'clock.

② We play soccer } during / (for) { 2 hours.

③ We are tired } in / (after) { the picnic.

④ I fall asleep } (during) / for { the class.

Ⓐ
p. 50

① I read a book ___for___ 1 hour a day.

② I stay in England ___during___ the summer vacation.

③ He dries his body ___after___ shower.

④ I have to arrive at school ___before___ 9 o'clock.

Ⓑ
p. 50

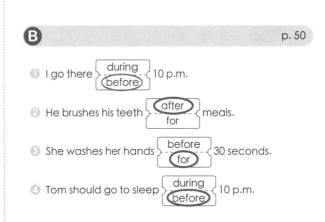

① I go there } during / (before) { 10 p.m.

② He brushes his teeth } (after) / for { meals.

③ She washes her hands } (before) / for { 30 seconds.

④ Tom should go to sleep } during / (before) { 10 p.m.

True? False?

① Summer comes after spring. TRUE

② Babies usually sleep for 12 hours. TRUE

③ People usually go to the beach during summer vacation. TRUE

④ Wednesday comes before Tuesday. FALSE

up, down, into, out of

Quick Check-Up p. 52

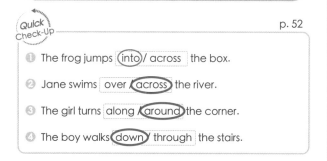

① The frog jumps (into)/ across the box.

② Jane swims over / (across) the river.

③ The girl turns along / (around) the corner.

④ The boy walks (down) / through the stairs.

A
p. 53

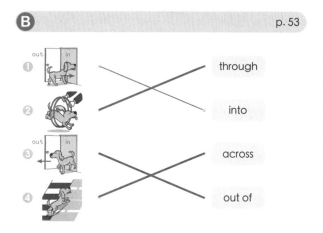

A ball bounces (into) the box.
It bounces (out of) the box.
It rolls (down) the hill.
It rolls (along) the road.
Catch it.

B
p. 53

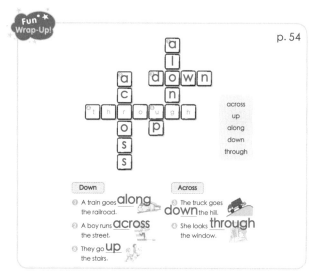

① through
② into
③ across
④ out of

Fun Wrap-Up!
p. 54

across
up
along
down
through

Down
① A train goes **along** the railroad.
② A boy runs **across** the street.
⑤ They go **up** the stairs.

Across
③ The truck goes **down** the hill.
④ She looks **through** the window.

to, for

Quick Check-Up p. 55

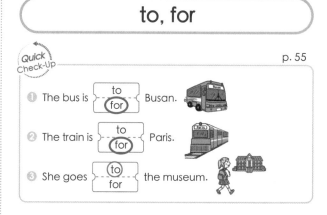

① The bus is to / (for) Busan.

② The train is to / (for) Paris.

③ She goes (to) / for the museum.

A
p. 56

① I go __to__ New York.

② She comes __to__ my office.

③ I must go __to__ the north.

④ The airplane is leaving __for__ Chicago.

⑤ The man runs __to__ the school.

B
p. 56

① The birds fly __to__ the south.

② The girl leaves __for__ China.

③ Is this train __for__ Seoul?

④ He runs __to__ the station.

⑤ I go __to__ the airport.

to
1, 4, 5

for
2, 3

Fun Wrap-Up!
p. 57

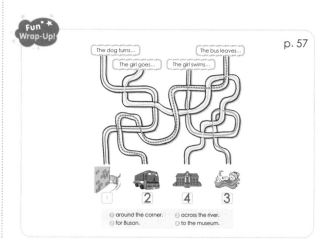

The dog turns...   The bus leaves...
The girl goes...   The girl swims...

① around the corner.   ③ across the river.
② for Busan.   ④ to the museum.

Lesson 30 There is, There are

긍정문

Quick Check-Up p. 58

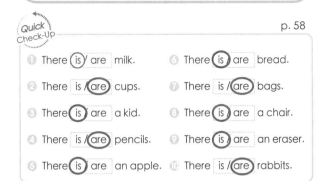

1. There (is) / are milk.
2. There is / (are) cups.
3. There (is) / are a kid.
4. There is / (are) pencils.
5. There (is) / are an apple.
6. There (is) / are bread.
7. There is / (are) bags.
8. There (is) / are a chair.
9. There (is) / are an eraser.
10. There is / (are) rabbits.

A p. 59

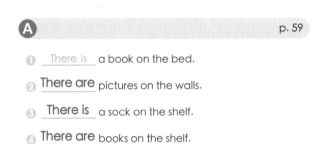

1. _There is_ a book on the bed.
2. **There are** pictures on the walls.
3. **There is** a sock on the shelf.
4. **There are** books on the shelf.

B p. 59

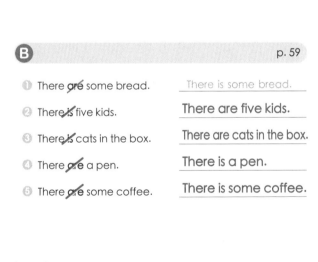

1. There ~~are~~ some bread. — _There is some bread._
2. There ~~is~~ five kids. — **There are five kids.**
3. There ~~is~~ cats in the box. — **There are cats in the box.**
4. There ~~are~~ a pen. — **There is a pen.**
5. There ~~are~~ some coffee. — **There is some coffee.**

Fun Wrap-Up! p. 60

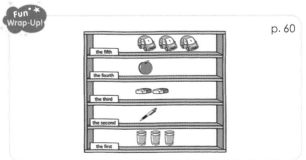

부정문, 의문문

Quick Check-Up p. 61

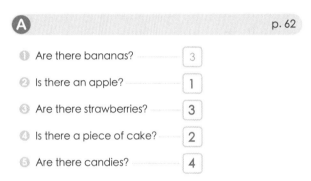

1. There ____ are ✓ books ____ in the bookcase.
2. There ____ is ✓ a vase ____ on the desk.
3. There ____ is ✓ a piece of pizza ____ on the table.
4. There ____ are ✓ pears ____ on the plate.

A p. 62

1. Are there bananas? — 3
2. Is there an apple? — 1
3. Are there strawberries? — 3
4. Is there a piece of cake? — 2
5. Are there candies? — 4

B p. 62

1. There **not is** my pillow on the bed.
   There is not my pillow on the bed.
2. There **are ~~not~~** his book under the bed.
   There is not his book under the bed.
3. Are ~~dolls there~~ on the shelf?
   Are there dolls on the shelf?

Fun Wrap-Up! p. 63

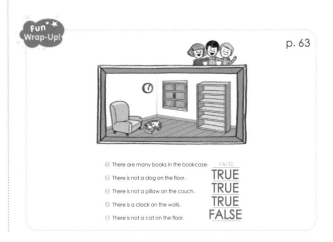

1. There are many books in the bookcase. — FALSE
2. There is not a dog on the floor. — TRUE
3. There is not a pillow on the couch. — TRUE
4. There is a clock on the walls. — TRUE
5. There is not a cat on the floor. — FALSE

A   p. 64

1   I get up _____ the morning.
    ① at   ②ⓘn   ③ on

2   I get up _____ 7 o'clock.
    ① on   ②at   ③ in

3   Summer vacation starts _____ July 3.
    ① in   ②on   ③ at

4   The train is _____ Paris.
    ① to   ②for   ③ down

5   The girl leaves _____ China.
    ①for   ② at   ③ to

B   p. 64

1   The dog is ____in____ the box.

2   The rabbit is __in front of__ the box.

3   The dog is ____under____ the table.

4   The box is ____between____ the rabbits.

C   p. 65

1   there / Are / strawberries?
    Are there strawberries?

2   is / a / There / on the table. / book
    There is a book on the table.

3   cats / are / There / in the box.
    There are cats in the box.

4   is / pillow / not / on the bed. / There / my
    There is not my pillow on the bed.

D   *Answers vary.*   p. 65

1   Where do you live?
    I live in Seoul.

2   What time do you get up in the morning?
    I get up at 7.

3   What do you do before dinner?
    I do my homework.

4   What do you usually do during summer vacation?
    I visit my grandmother.

Can, Be able to 1

긍정문

p. 68

Quick Check-Up

① John can (ride)/ rides a bike.

② They is /(are) able to play tennis.

③ Tom are (is) able to swimming /(swim).

④ Obama can plays /(play) soccer well.

A

p. 69

① can / Tom / play tennis.

Tom can play tennis.

② am able to / I / read books.

I am able to read books.

③ ski. / able to / I / am

I am able to ski.

④ Mom / sing / well. / can

Mom can sing well.

B

p. 69

① We can goes fishing. We can go fishing.

② She can plays the violin. She can play the violin.

③ I are able to swim. I am able to swim.

④ They is able to ski. They are able to ski.

Fun Wrap-Up!

p. 70

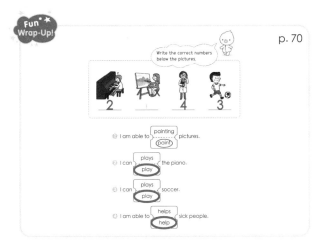

Write the correct numbers below the pictures.

2   1   4   3

① I am able to painting / (paint) pictures.

② I can plays / (play) the piano.

③ I can plays / (play) soccer.

④ I am able to helps / (help) sick people.

부정문

p. 71

Quick Check-Up

① Jane (is not)/ am not able to fly.

② They (can not)/ not can run fast.

③ I (am not)/ are not able to read Chinese.

④ He can't plays / (play) soccer well.

⑤ You not can (can't) ride a bike.

A

p. 72

① He / is / not / make / able to / a desk.

He is not able to make a desk.

② not / I / am / drive a car. / able to

I am not able to drive a car.

③ cannot / They / play tennis.

They cannot play tennis.

④ able to / I / read English. / not / am

I am not able to read English.

B

p. 72

① He ___can___ not run fast.

② I am ___not___ able to speak Chinese.

③ She is not ___able to___ play the piano.

④ Jenny ___is___ not able to play tennis.

Fun Wrap-Up!

p. 73

can   can't

① Birds ___can___ fly, but they ___can't___ swim.

② Fish can swim, but they can't run.

③ Rabbits can hop, but they can't swim.

④ Turtles can't walk fast, but they can swim.

⑤ Monkeys can't ride a bike, but they can climb trees.

Can, Be able to 2

<table>
<tr><td>

can 의문문

</td><td>

be able to 의문문

</td></tr>
</table>

Quick Check-Up   p. 74

① Can he ride a bike?
  ☑ Yes, he can.
  ☐ No, he can't.

② Can he fly a kite?
  ☑ Yes, he can.
  ☐ No, he can't.

③ Can they play baseball?
  ☑ Yes, they can.
  ☐ No, they can't.

Quick Check-Up   p. 77

① Is he able to ride a bike?
  ☑ Yes, he is.
  ☐ Yes, he can.

② Is he able to fly a kite?
  ☑ Yes, he is.
  ☐ Yes, he can.

③ Are they able to play baseball?
  ☑ Yes, they are.
  ☐ Yes, they can.

A   p. 75

① Can you sing?   Yes, they can.
② Can they go fishing?   No, I can't.
③ Can Suzy play the piano?   No, she can't.
④ Can he dance?   Yes, he can.
⑤ Can you read Chinese?   Yes, I can.

B   p. 75

① Can she swim?
  - Yes, __she can__ .

② Can they dance?
  - Yes, __they can__ .

③ Can she draw a picture?
  - Yes, __she can__ .

A   p. 78

① Is / able to / he / play the piano?
  __Is he able to play the piano?__

② Are / able to / swim? / you
  __Are you able to swim?__

③ they / speak / English? / able to / Are
  __Are they able to speak English?__

B   p. 78

① __Is__ a bird able to fly?   - Yes, it __is__ .
② Is he __able to__ play the violin? - No, he __isn't__ .
③ Are they __able to__ ski?   - __No__ , they aren't.
④ Are you able to run fast?   - Yes, we __are__ .

Fun Wrap-Up!   p. 76

	⚽	🎾	🎹	⛷
Tom	×	○	○	×
Peter	○	×	○	×
James	○	×	○	×
Scott	×	○	○	×

① Can Tom play soccer?   - No, he can't.
② Can Peter play tennis? No, he can't.
③ Can James ski?   No, he can't.
④ Can Scott play the piano? Yes, he can.

(can't=can not/cannot)

Fun Wrap-Up!   p. 79

Yes, it is.   No, it isn't.

Is a bird able to fly? Is a cheetah able to run fast? Is a rabbit able to hop?
Yes, it is.   Yes, it is.   Yes, it is.

Is a cat able to swim? Is an elephant able to stomp?   Is a snake able to walk?
No, it isn't.   Yes, it is.   No, it isn't.

Is a horse able to drive a car? Is a frog able to swim? Is a mouse able to talk?
No, it isn't.   Yes, it is.   No, it isn't.

① What letter did you make?   T
② How many red boxes are there?   5
③ How many blue boxes are there?   4

Must, Have/Has to

긍정문

Quick
Check-Up
p. 80

1. He must (work)/ works tonight.
2. I (have to)/ has to wash my hands.
3. She (has to)/ have to tell the truth.
4. They (must go)/ go must to school.
5. Tom has to brushes /(brush) his teeth.
6. He (has to)/ have to go to bed early.

A

p. 81

1. He __has__ __to__ wash his face.
2. You __must__ listen to your mom.
3. They __have__ __to__ keep the rules.
4. I __have__ __to__ share this bench.
5. She __has__ __to__ come home early.

B

p. 81

1. I must (drink)/ drinks water every day.
2. Sam have to /(has to) wear uniform.
3. They (have to)/ has to follow the rules.
4. You must (stop)/ stops before crossing roads.
5. Suzy have to /(has to) finish her work by 9 p.m.

Fun
Wrap-Up!
p. 82

__You have to wash your hands.__

__He has to practice tennis.__

부정문

Quick
Check-Up
p. 83

1. He don't /(doesn't) have to work weekends.
2. We mustnot /(must not) run in the classroom.
3. You (don't)/ doesn't have to go fishing with me.
4. You (mustn't)/ mustnot touch this.
5. We (don't)/ doesn't have to go to bed early.

A

p. 84

1. We _____ must __✓__ hit _____ other people.
2. You _____ must __✓__ make _____ a noise.
3. They _____ do __✓__ have to be here.
4. She _____ does __✓__ have to choose this.

B

p. 84

1. You must not run in the classroom.
2. We must not cry.
3. She must take care of her cat.
4. You don't have to read this book.

Fun
Wrap-Up!
p. 85

☑Sam	□Suzy	□Tom
We must help each other.	You don't have to listen to your teacher.	You must not do your homework.
☑Mike	□Minji	☑John
We have to keep the rules.	We must run in the classroom.	You must not tease your friends.
☑David	☑Susan	□Max
We must not hit friends.	I have to take care of my pets.	You must not clean your room.

Write the names of the good children.
Sam   __Mike__   __John__
__David__   __Susan__

Should, Had better

should

Quick Check-Up   p. 86

1. You (should listen)/ listen should carefully.

2. I (should wash)/ wash should my hands.

3. She should not makes /(make) a noise.

4. We (shouldn't)/ shouldnot waste money.

A
p. 87

1. My hands are dirty. I ___should___ wash my hands.

2. You look tired. You __should__ take a rest.

3. He has a headache. He __should__ go to hospital.

4. It is too hot. You __shouldn't__ touch it.

B
p. 87

1. You should ~~are~~ nice to your friends.

   You should be nice to your friends.

2. Children ~~shouldnot~~ tell a lie.

   Children should not[shouldn't] tell a lie.

3. Tom should not ~~wastes~~ water.

   Tom should not waste water.

Fun Wrap-Up!
p. 88

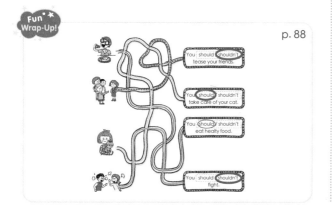

You | should /(shouldn't) tease your friends.

You/(should)/ shouldn't take care of your cat.

You/(should)/ shouldn't eat healty food.

You | should /(shouldn't) fight.

had better

Quick Check-Up   p. 89

1. (had better call)/ had better to call

2. had not better study /(had better not study)

3. (had better get up)/ had better getting up

4. had not better eat /(had better not eat)

A
p. 90

1. The train leaves in 5 minutes.

   You ___had better___ hurry up.

2. It's too noisy. You __had better not__ make a noise.

3. It's cloudy. You __had better__ take an umbrella.

B
p. 90

1. had better / do / You / your homework.

   You had better do your homework.

2. save / You / water. / had better

   You had better save water.

3. eat / You / junk food. / had better not

   You had better not eat junk food.

Fun Wrap-Up!
p. 91

You had better drink water instead of coke.

You had better not watch TV too much.

You had better not eat junk food.

Basic Test

A   p. 92

1 He _____ not run fast.
   ① able to   ②(can)   ③ not

2 She is not _____ play the piano.
   ① able   ②(able to)   ③ can

3 I am _____ able to speak Chinese.
   ①(not)   ② can   ③ cannot

4 She _____ come home early.
   ① have to   ②(has to)   ③ able to

5 He _____ work weekends.
   ① don't have to ②(doesn't have to) ③ don't has to

B   p. 92

1 I am ___**able to**___ ski.

2 Jane ___**is not able to**___ fly.

3 We ___**must not**___ run in the classroom.

4 It's cloudy. You ___**had better**___ take an umbrella.

C   p. 93

1 can / can't / run. / swim, / Fish / but / they
   Fish can swim, but they can't run.

2 play / Scott / the / Can / piano?
   Can Scott play the piano?

3 You / have to / go fishing / with me. / don't
   You don't have to go fishing with me.

4 should / be / You / to / nice / your friends.
   You should be nice to your friends.

D *Answers vary.*   p. 93

1 What can you do well?
   I can play the piano well.

2 Are you able to speak English?
   Yes, I am.

3 What do you have to do every day?
   I have to feed my cat every day.

4 What should you do when you feel tired?
   I should take a rest.

현재 시제의 쓰임

p. 96

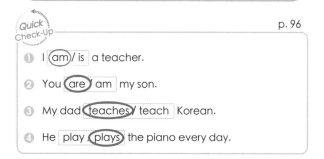

① I (am)/ is a teacher.

② You (are)/ am my son.

③ My dad (teaches)/ teach Korean.

④ He play /(plays) the piano every day.

A
p. 97

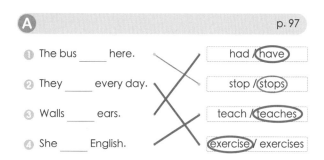

① The bus _____ here.　　had /(have)

② They _____ every day.　　stop /(stops)

③ Walls _____ ears.　　teach /(teaches)

④ She _____ English.　　(exercise)/ exercises

B
p. 97

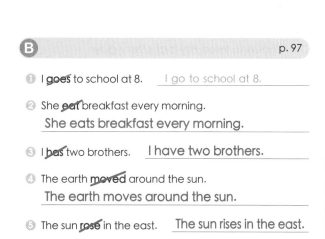

① I goes to school at 8.　　I go to school at 8.

② She eat breakfast every morning.
She eats breakfast every morning.

③ I has two brothers.　　I have two brothers.

④ The earth moved around the sun.
The earth moves around the sun.

⑤ The sun rose in the east.　　The sun rises in the east.

Answers vary.

p. 98

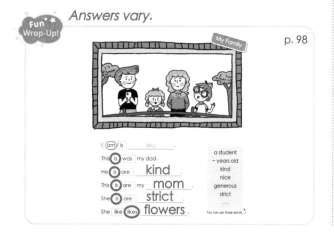

현재 시제 수 일치

p. 99

☑ He likes apples.　　☑ We play in the park.

☑ I wash my hands.　　☐ They goes home.

☑ She speaks English.　　☐ He go shopping.

☐ It am cute.　　☐ David are happy.

A
p. 100

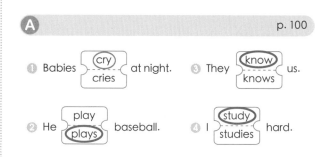

① Babies (cry)/ cries at night.　③ They (know)/ knows us.

② He play /(plays) baseball.　④ I (study)/ studies hard.

B
p. 100

① I __fly__ a kite. She __flies__ a kite.

② They __miss__ you. He **misses** you.

③ The teacher **teaches** math. They **teach** math.

④ Tom **exercises** every day. We **exercise** every day.

⑤ I __am__ in the room. They __are__ in the kitchen.

⑥ She __is__ happy. We __are__ happy.

p. 101

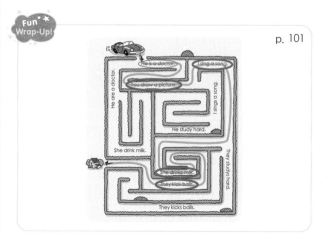

현재 시제 2

부정문

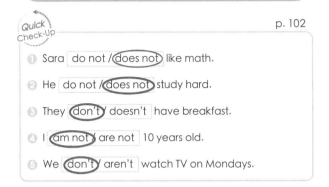

Quick Check-Up   p. 102

1. Sara | do not /(does not) | like math.
2. He | do not /(does not) | study hard.
3. They |(don't)/ doesn't | have breakfast.
4. I |(am not)/ are not | 10 years old.
5. We |(don't)/ aren't | watch TV on Mondays.

A   p. 103

1. does / She / not / smile.
   She does not smile.

2. a policeman. / is / He / not
   He is not a policeman.

3. wear / Sally / glasses. / not / does
   Sally does not wear glasses.

B   p. 103

1. She ___does not___ drink coffee.
2. Sam ___does not___ look angry.
3. They ___do not___ like games.
4. We ___do not___ have dinner at school.
5. Nick and Sue ___do not___ want to have a pet.
6. I ___do not___ get up early.

Fun Wrap-Up!   p. 104

| don't | doesn't | isn't | aren't |

1. Birds ___don't swim___ , but they fly. (swim)
2. A fish _____, but it swims. (run)   doesn't run
3. Rabbits _____ trees, but they hop. (climb)   don't climb
4. A turtle _____, and it is slow. (fast)   isn't fast
5. Monkeys _____, but they climb trees. (fly)   don't fly
6. Cows _____ meat, but they eat grass. (eat)   don't eat

의문문

Quick Check-Up   p. 105

1. (Do)/Are you play tennis?
2. (Are)/Do they students?
3. (Are)/Is you angry?
4. (Does)/Do he need them?
5. Is/(Does) she 8 years old?
6. (Does)/Do he want a cat?

A   p. 106

1. ___is___ your mom tall?
2. ___Am___ I wrong?
3. ___Does___ she get up early?
4. ___Do___ we have homework today?

B   p. 106

1. Do they look happy?
   No, they don't.

2. Does he fly a kite?
   Yes, he does.

3. Are you tired?
   Yes, I am.

4. Is it rainy outside?
   No, it isn't[is not].

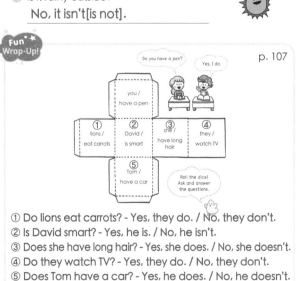

Fun Wrap-Up!   p. 107

① Do lions eat carrots? - Yes, they do. / No, they don't.
② Is David smart? - Yes, he is. / No, he isn't.
③ Does she have long hair? - Yes, she does. / No, she doesn't.
④ Do they watch TV? - Yes, they do. / No, they don't.
⑤ Does Tom have a car? - Yes, he does. / No, he doesn't.

현재 진행형이란?

p. 108

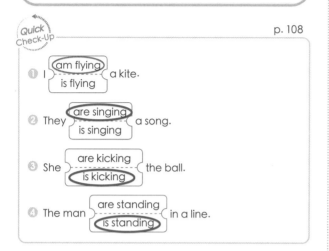

① I (am flying) / is flying a kite.

② They (are singing) / is singing a song.

③ She are kicking / (is kicking) the ball.

④ The man are standing / (is standing) in a line.

A

p. 109

① I __am taking__ a rest now. (take)

② She __is eating__ a piece of pizza now. (eat)

③ He __is playing__ soccer. (play)

④ The sun __is shining__. (shine)

B

p. 109

① He ~~studying~~ math hard.   He is studying math hard.

② I ~~am make~~ a cake now.   I am making a cake now.

③ She ~~washing~~ her hands.   She is washing her hands.

④ They ~~is waiting~~ for a bus.   They are waiting for a bus.

⑤ The dog ~~is bark~~.   The dog is barking.

p. 110

현재 진행형 vs 단순 현재

p. 111

☐ He is having a car.   ☑ We are running.

☑ She is speaking Chinese.   ☑ I am washing my hands.

☑ You are driving now.   ☑ They are going home.

☐ He is needing a book.   ☐ He is believing it.

A

p. 112

① He (needs) / is needing to sleep.

② I (have) / am having a flower.

③ Jane (likes) / is liking apples.

④ They (want) / are wanting a big house.

⑤ We (hate) / are hating each other.

B

p. 112

① Sam __knows__ you. (know)

② Jane __is talking__ on the phone now. (talk)

③ Dad __is cooking__ dinner now. (cook)

④ They __are helping__ their friends now. (help)

⑤ He __believes__ in God. (believe)

⑥ We __are listening__ to music now. (listen)

p. 113

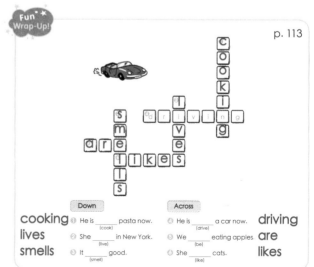

Down

cooking ① He is _____ pasta now. (cook)

lives ② She _____ in New York. (live)

smells ③ It _____ good. (smell)

Across

④ He is _____ a car now. (drive) driving

⑤ We _____ eating apples. (be) are

⑥ She _____ cats. (like) likes

현재 진행형 형태 (1)

Quick Check-Up   p. 114

☑ She is making a chair.   ☑ I am watering the plants.

☐ They are danceing.   ☑ We are coming!

☑ I am going to the zoo.   ☑ I am flying a kite.

☐ Mom is haveing lunch.   ☐ She is studing math.

☑ Dad is cooking supper.   ☑ They are walking.

A   p. 115

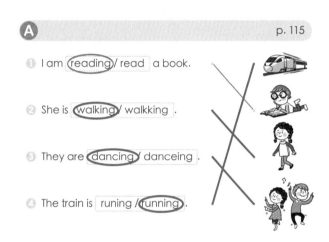

1. I am ~~reading~~/ read a book.

2. She is ~~walking~~/ walkking .

3. They are ~~dancing~~/ danceing .

4. The train is runing /~~running~~ .

B   p. 115

1. She __is__ __making__ a sandcastle now. (make)

2. We __are__ __watering__ the garden. (water)

3. They __are__ __studying__ English. (study)

4. The man __is__ __coming__ to me. (come)

5. Sam __is__ __parking__ his car. (park)

Fun Wrap-Up!   p. 116

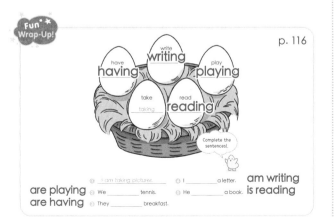

are playing
are having

am writing
is reading

현재 진행형 형태 (2)

Quick Check-Up   p. 117

☑ They are running.   ☐ She is lieing on the bed.

☑ He is lying on the grass. ☐ He is runing.

☐ The car is stoping.   ☐ He is siting on a sofa.

☑ I am sitting on a bench.   ☑ My flower is dying.

☑ They are putting the books on the desk.

A   p. 118

1. The man is ~~putting~~/ puting his jacket on the chair.

2. They are ~~sitting~~/ siting on the bench.

3. She is ~~chatting~~/ chating with her friend.

B   p. 118

1. My dad __is__ __sitting__ on the sofa.

2. Max __is__ __running__ with his friends.

3. John __is__ __lying__ on the bed.

4. He __is__ __cutting__ the paper.

5. We __are__ __swimming__ in the river.

Fun Wrap-Up!   p. 119

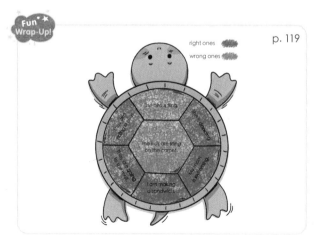

right ones
wrong ones

Lesson 39 현재 진행형: 부정문

부정문

Quick Check-Up — p. 120

① I ___ am ✓ looking at the monkeys.

② Paul ___ is ✓ walking on the road.

③ They ___ are ✓ watching TV in the room.

④ We ___ are ✓ painting on the walls.

⑤ She ___ is ✓ talking ___ on the phone.

A
p. 121

① You (are not walking)/ not are walking on the road.

② I (am not studying)/ am studying not math now.

③ Children not are watching /(are not watching) TV.

④ Evan (is not reading)/ is reading not a comic book.

⑤ I not am dancing /(am not dancing) here.

B
p. 121

① Mom _is not packing_ her lunch. (pack)

② He is __not playing__ the guitar. (play)

③ They are __not writing__ letters. (write)

④ I am __not washing__ my hands. (wash)

⑤ David is __not doing__ his homework. (do)

Fun Wrap-Up! — p. 122

① Dad _is not_ watching TV.
He is cooking lunch.

② Mom __is not__ cooking lunch.
She is reading a book.

③ Grandma __is not__ having a meal.
She is drinking a cup of coffee.

부정문 줄임말

Quick Check-Up — p. 123

A
p. 124

① not / She's / cooking / pasta.
   She's not cooking pasta.

② working / not / on the computer. / He's
   __He's not working on the computer.__

③ Grandpa. / We're / visiting / not
   __We're not visiting Grandpa.__

④ riding / not / I'm / a bike.
   __I'm not riding a bike.__

B
p. 124

① You are not drawing cars. ○ _You aren't drawing cars._

② He is not driving a car. ○ __He isn't driving a car.__

③ She is not taking pictures. ○ __She isn't taking pictures.__

④ I am not taking a bus. ○ __I'm not taking a bus.__

Fun Wrap-Up! — p. 125

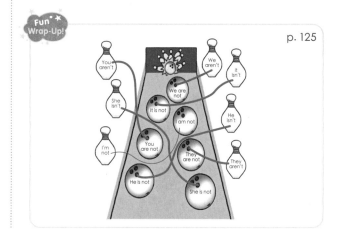

질문하기

p. 126

Quick Check-Up

① ☑ Are you watching TV?

　☐ Are you watch TV?

② ☐ Is he sing a song?

　☑ Is he singing a song?

③ ☐ Does she studying hard?

　☑ Is she studying hard?

A

p. 127

① You are having dinner. → <u>Are you having dinner</u> ?

② He is cleaning his room. → **Is he cleaning his room** ?

③ They are going to the market.
→ **Are they going to the market** ?

④ Tom is playing with blocks.
→ **Is Tom playing with blocks** ?

⑤ She is taking a nap. → **Is she taking a nap** ?

B

p. 127

① <u>Are you playing</u> the guitar? (you, play)

② **Is he working** on this project? (he, work)

③ **Is she watching** TV? (she, watch)

④ **Are they playing** basketball? (they, play)

⑤ **Is Jimmy dancing** with Nancy? (Jimmy, dance)

⑥ **Are you studying** English? (you, study)

Fun Wrap-Up!

p. 128

They are playing with a ball.

○ _____ ?

Are they playing with a ball

대답하기

p. 129

Quick Check-Up

① Is he reading a book?
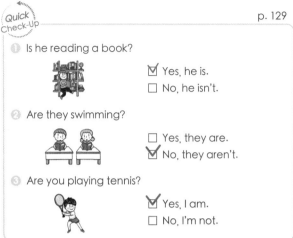
☑ Yes, he is.
☐ No, he isn't.

② Are they swimming?
☐ Yes, they are.
☑ No, they aren't.

③ Are you playing tennis?
☑ Yes, I am.
☐ No, I'm not.

A

p. 130

① Are you learning Japanese? - Yes, <u>I am</u> .

② Are you dancing? - No, **I'm not[am not]/ we aren't[are not]**

③ Are you eating snacks? - Yes, **I am/we are**

④ Is the cat sleeping? - No, **it isn't[is not]**.

⑤ Is he taking a shower? - Yes, **he is** .

B

p. 130

① <u>Are</u> you reading a book? - Yes, I <u>am</u> .

② **Are** they jumping? - Yes, they **are** .

③ **Is** she thinking about it? - No, she **isn't** .

④ **Are** they moving the desk? - No, they **aren't** .

Fun Wrap-Up!

p. 131

My Family

① Is Dad watching TV? - No, he isn't.

② Is Mom reading a book? - **Yes, she is.**

③ Is Grandma having a meal? - **No, she isn't[is not].**

④ Is Grandpa sleeping? - **Yes, he is.**

· Basic Test ·

A
p. 132

1 Sara _____ like math.
  ① does not   ② do not   ③ is not

2 They _____ have breakfast.
  ① doesn't   ② don't   ③ aren't

3 John is _____ on the bed.
  ① lieng   ② lying   ③ lieing

4 He _____ math hard.
  ① are studying   ② is studying   ③ am studying

5 They _____ for a bus.
  ① are waiting   ② am waiting   ③ is waiting

B
p. 132

1 The dog is ___barking___ .

2 Are you ___having___ dinner?

3 Jane is talking on the phone ___now___ .

4 The earth ___moves___ around the sun.

C
p. 133

1 breakfast / She / every morning. / eats
  She eats breakfast every morning.

2 it / rainy / Is / outside?
  Is it rainy outside?

3 a bench. / I / sitting / on / am
  I am sitting on a bench.

4 not / on the computer. / working / He's
  He's not working on the computer.

D   Answers vary.
p. 133

1 Is it sunny outside?
  Yes, it is.

2 What time do you go to school?
  I go to school at 8.

3 Are you watching TV now?
  No, I am not.

4 What are you doing now?
  I am studying English.

Activity Cards & Paper Cube

Lesson 24 p. 20

rarely	sometimes	never	always
often	usually	seldom	

Lesson 28 p. 48

the evening	April	Sunday	2015
night	February	May 12	summer
Wednesday	the afternoon	Christmas Day	fall
06:00	noon	June	spring

Lesson 28 p. 51

TRUE	FALSE	TRUE	FALSE
TRUE	FALSE	TRUE	FALSE

Lesson 34 p. 91

You had better not eat junk food.	You had better not watch TV too much.	You had better drink water instead of coke.

Activity Cards & Paper Cube

Lesson 36 p. 107

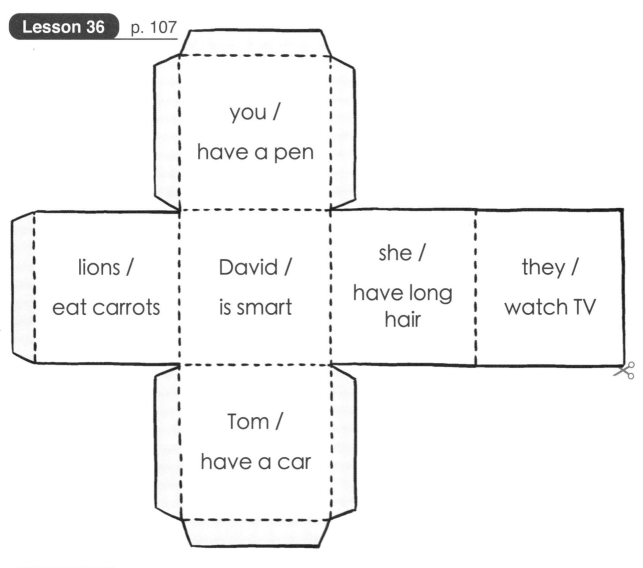

you /
have a pen

lions /
eat carrots

David /
is smart

she /
have long
hair

they /
watch TV

Tom /
have a car

Lesson 40 p. 128

부록

Appendix

영어의 8품사

명사	사람, 동물, 사물, 장소 등의 이름을 나타내는 말	
	보통명사	girl, man, teacher, car, dog, mouse, pen, school
	고유명사	Abraham Lincoln, Christmas Day, April, Friday, France
	물질명사	water, coffee, juice, flour, salt, air, bread, butter, gold
	추상명사	love, health, peace, beauty, friendship, art, music
대명사	명사를 대신하는 말	
	인칭대명사	I, you, he, she, it, we, they
	지시대명사	this, that, these, those
동사	동작이나 상태를 나타내는 말	
	be동사	am, are, is, was, were
	일반동사	go, eat, run, study, make, want, like
형용사	색깔, 크기, 상태, 수량 등을 나타내는 말	
	green, red, small, big, dirty, clean, many, much, a lot of	

부사	동작이나 상태를 더 자세히 설명하는 말
	fast, hard, slowly, very, really, too, now, here
접속사	단어와 단어, 구와 구, 절과 절, 문장과 문장을 연결하는 말
	and, but, or, before, after, so, because
전치사	명사나 대명사 앞에 놓여 장소, 시간, 방향 등을 나타내는 말
	in, under, on, behind, in front of, by, between, at
감탄사	기쁨, 슬픔, 놀라움 따위의 감정, 부름, 응답 등을 나타내는 말
	wow, oh, hey, dear, ouch, oops

❋ **품사**: 단어를 기능, 형태, 의미에
따라 나누어 놓은 문장의 기본 요소
❋ 단어 < 구 < 절 < 문장

인칭대명사

수	인칭	주격 ~은/는/이/가	소유격 ~의	목적격 ~을(를),~에게	소유대명사 ~의 것
단수	1인칭	I	my	me	mine
	2인칭	you	your	you	yours
	3인칭	he	his	him	his
		she	her	her	hers
		it	its	it	its
복수	1인칭	we	our	us	ours
	2인칭	you	your	you	yours
	3인칭	they	their	them	theirs

be동사

수	인칭	주어	현재형	과거형
단수	1인칭	I	am	was
	2인칭	you	are	were
	3인칭	he, she, it	is	was
복수	1인칭	we	are	were
	2인칭	you		
	3인칭	they		

축약

대명사+be동사		대명사+will		동사+not	
I am	I'm	I will	I'll	is not	isn't
you are	you're	you will	you'll	are not	aren't
he is	he's	he will	he'll	was not	wasn't
she is	she's	she will	she'll	were not	weren't
it is	it's	it will	it'll	will not	won't
we are	we're	we will	we'll	do not	don't
they are	they're	they will	they'll	does not	doesn't
that is	that's	that will	that'll	did not	didn't
who is	who's	who will	who'll	can not	can't
				must not	mustn't

❊ **1인칭** : 나, 우리 ❊ **2인칭** : 너, 너희

❊ **3인칭** : 1인칭 , 2인칭을 제외한 나머지 모두

❊ **단수** : 명사가 하나 있을 때

❊ **복수** : 명사가 둘 이상 여럿 있을 때

❜ 아포스트로피 :
생략을 나타내는 기호

 **명사의 복수형**

규칙형	대부분의 단수 명사 **+s**
	ba**gs**, cat**s**, horse**s**, teacher**s**, friend**s**, kangaroo**s**, radio**s**
	s, ch, sh, x, 자음+o로 끝나는 명사 **+es**
	bus**es**, bench**es**, dish**es**, wish**es**, fox**es**, tomato**es**, potato**es**
	자음+y로 끝나는 명사 **y → i+es**
	baby → bab**ies**, city → cit**ies**, lady → lad**ies**, berry → berr**ies**
	f나 fe로 끝나는 명사 **f, fe → v+es**
	leaf → lea**ves**, life → li**ves**, knife → kni**ves**, wife → wi**ves**
불규칙형	형태가 바뀌는 명사
	child → children, foot → feet, mouse → mice, tooth → teeth
	단수와 복수의 형태가 같은 명사
	deer, fish, sheep
	복수형으로 쓰는 명사(짝을 이루는 명사)
	pants, shoes, socks, scissors, glasses, shorts, pajamas

일반동사의 현재형 주어가 3인칭 단수인 경우

대부분의 동사 **동사원형+s**

like**s**, buy**s**, play**s**, sing**s**, come**s**, make**s**, cook**s**, exercise**s**

o, s, x, ch, sh로 끝나는 동사 **동사원형+es**

go**es**, do**es**, pass**es**, kiss**es**, fix**es**, teach**es**, catch**es**, wash**es**

자음+y로 끝나는 동사 **y → i+es**

cry → cr**ies**, try → tr**ies**, study → stud**ies**, fly → fl**ies**

불규칙 변화

have → has

일반동사+ing

대부분의 동사 **동사원형+ing**

do**ing**, read**ing**, eat**ing**, drink**ing**, go**ing**, walk**ing**, study**ing**, watch**ing**

e로 끝나는 동사 **e를 빼고+ing**

write → writ**ing**, make → mak**ing**, come → com**ing**, dance → danc**ing**

ie로 끝나는 동사 **ie → y+ing**

lie → l**ying**, die → d**ying**, tie → t**ying**

단모음+단자음으로 끝나는 동사 **자음 하나 더 쓰고+ing**

put → put**ting**, cut → cut**ting**, stop → stop**ping**, run → run**ning**

숫자 읽기

기수 개수를 나타내는 수

13	thirteen	30	thirty
14	fourteen	40	forty
15	fifteen	50	fifty
16	sixteen	60	sixty
17	seventeen	70	seventy
18	eighteen	80	eighty
19	nineteen	90	ninety
20	twenty	100	one-hundred

❀ 일, 이, 삼,
하나, 둘, 셋은 기수!
❀ 첫 번째, 두 번째,
세 번째는 서수!

서수 순서를 나타내는 수

1st	first	11th	eleventh	30th	thirtieth
2nd	second	12th	twelfth	40th	fortieth
3rd	third	13th	thirteenth	50th	fiftieth
4th	fourth	14th	fourteenth	60th	sixtieth
5th	fifth	15th	fifteenth	70th	seventieth
6th	sixth	16th	sixteenth	80th	eightieth
7th	seventh	17th	seventeenth	90th	ninetieth
8th	eighth	18th	eighteenth	100th	one-hundredth
9th	ninth	19th	nineteenth	101st	one-hundred (and) first
10th	tenth	20th	twentieth		

My Grammar Note

❀ 빈칸에 알맞은 인칭대명사를 써 넣으세요.

수	인칭	주격 ~은/는/이/가	소유격 ~의	목적격 ~을(를), ~에게	소유대명사 ~의 것
단수	1인칭 나				
	2인칭 너				
	3인칭 그				
	3인칭 그녀				
	3인칭 그것				
복수	1인칭 우리				
	2인칭 너희들				
	3인칭 그들				

❀ 빈칸에 알맞은 be동사를 써 넣으세요.

수	인칭	주어	현재형	과거형
단수	1인칭	I		
	2인칭	you		
	3인칭	he, she, it		
복수	1인칭	we		
	2인칭	you		
	3인칭	they		

My Grammar Note

❁ 빈칸에 알맞은 축약형을 써 넣으세요.

I am	I will	is not
you are	you will	are not
he is	he will	was not
she is	she will	were not
it is	it will	will not
we are	we will	does not
they are	they will	did not
that is	that will	can not
who is	who will	must not

❁ 빈칸에 알맞은 복수형을 써 넣으세요.

bag	dish	life
book	wish	knife
cat	fox	wife
horse	tomato	child
teacher	potato	foot
friend	baby	mouse
kangaroo	city	tooth
radio	lady	deer
bus	berry	fish
bench	leaf	sheep

✿ 빈칸에 알맞은 **현재형**을 써 넣으세요. (주어가 3인칭 단수일 경우)

like	kiss
buy	fix
play	teach
sing	catch
come	wash
make	cry
cook	try
exercise	study
go	fly
do	have

✿ 빈칸에 알맞은 **동사원형+ing** 형태를 써 넣으세요.

do	come
read	dance
eat	lie
drink	die
go	tie
walk	put
study	cut
watch	stop
write	run

My Grammar Note

✿ 빈칸에 알맞은 서수를 써 넣으세요.

1st		16th	
2nd		17th	
3rd		18th	
4th		19th	
5th		20th	
6th		30th	
7th		40th	
8th		50th	
9th		60th	
10th		70th	
11th		80th	
12th		90th	
13th		100th	
14th		101st	
15th			

Answers

p. 171

수	인칭		주격 ~은/는/이/가	소유격 ~의	목적격 ~을(를),~에게	소유대명사 ~의 것
단수	1인칭	나	I	my	me	mine
	2인칭	너	you	your	you	yours
	3인칭	그	he	his	him	his
	3인칭	그녀	she	her	her	hers
	3인칭	그것	it	its	it	its
복수	1인칭	우리	we	our	us	ours
	2인칭	너희들	you	your	you	yours
	3인칭	그들	they	their	them	theirs

p. 171

수	인칭	주어	현재형	과거형
단수	1인칭	I	am	was
	2인칭	you	are	were
	3인칭	he, she, it	is	was
복수	1인칭	we		
	2인칭	you	are	were
	3인칭	they		

p. 172

I am	I'm	I will	I'll	is not	isn't
you are	you're	you will	you'll	are not	aren't
he is	he's	he will	he'll	was not	wasn't
she is	she's	she will	she'll	were not	weren't
it is	it's	it will	it'll	will not	won't
we are	we're	we will	we'll	does not	doesn't
they are	they're	they will	they'll	did not	didn't
that is	that's	that will	that'll	can not	can't
who is	who's	who will	who'll	must not	mustn't

p. 172

bag	bags	dish	dishes	life	lives
book	books	wish	wishes	knife	knives
cat	cats	fox	foxes	wife	wives
horse	horses	tomato	tomatoes	child	children
teacher	teachers	potato	potatoes	foot	feet
friend	friends	baby	babies	mouse	mice
kangaroo	kangaroos	city	cities	tooth	teeth
radio	radios	lady	ladies	deer	deer
bus	buses	berry	berries	fish	fish
bench	benches	leaf	leaves	sheep	sheep

p. 173

like	likes	kiss	kisses
buy	buys	fix	fixes
play	plays	teach	teaches
sing	sings	catch	catches
come	comes	wash	washes
make	makes	cry	cries
cook	cooks	try	tries
exercise	exercises	study	studies
go	goes	fly	flies
do	does	have	has

p. 173

do	doing	come	coming
read	reading	dance	dancing
eat	eating	lie	lying
drink	drinking	die	dying
go	going	tie	tying
walk	walking	put	putting
study	studying	cut	cutting
watch	watching	stop	stopping
write	writing	run	running

p. 174

1st	first	16th	sixteenth
2nd	second	17th	seventeenth
3rd	third	18th	eighteenth
4th	fourth	19th	nineteenth
5th	fifth	20th	twentieth
6th	sixth	30th	thirtieth
7th	seventh	40th	fortieth
8th	eighth	50th	fiftieth
9th	ninth	60th	sixtieth
10th	tenth	70th	seventieth
11th	eleventh	80th	eightieth
12th	twelfth	90th	ninetieth
13th	thirteenth	100th	one-hundredth
14th	fourteenth	101st	one-hundred (and) first
15th	fifteenth		

MEMO